Feelings after Birth

This reprint has been funded through the generosity of NCT branches in Region 4: Beckenham & Penge and Molesley & Thames Ditton

Cover design
Tim McPhee
Book Production Consultants plc

Cover photograph
Louise O'Gorman Photography
0115 845 7949
0798547 2996
<u>www.louiseogormanphotography.com</u>

The **NCT** Book of Postnatal Depression

Feelings after Birth

Heather Welford

NCT Publishing

First published in 1998 by Thorsons/NCT Publishing

This edition published in 2002 by
NCT Publishing
25–27 High Street
Chesterton
Cambridge
CB4 1ND
www.nctpublishing.co.uk

© NCT Publishing 2002

Heather Welford asserts the moral right to
be identified as the author of this work

A catalogue record for this book
is available from the British Library

ISBN 0-9543018-0-3

Printed and bound in the UK by
ComPletE

Contents

Introduction

Postnatal depression is something that's likely to touch all our lives. You, or your partner, might have experienced it. Or your own mother may have done so. Or perhaps you have a friend, a sister, a neighbour who has suffered. You may be in a position to offer help and support to a postnatally depressed woman. Whatever the situation, this book will help you gain an understanding and an insight into the causes and effects of this condition.

I am especially pleased that this book has been able to look in some detail at the effect postnatal depression has on two other important groups of people – fathers, and the babies themselves. This was quite new stuff back in 1998 when the first edition of this book was published, particularly new in a book aimed at non-academic and non-specialist readers. It's still just as new now, and the effect of postnatal depression on the baby continues to be something that's rarely talked about. I don't think I recall one article about it, though Professor Robert Winston's compulsively watchable TV series, *A Child in Our Time* (BBC, began Spring 2001) touched on it a little.

The definition of postnatal depression brings its own problem. Calling postnatal depression an illness implies that it's rather similar to some sort of bodily malfunction that arrives out of nowhere, and that you are just unlucky to 'catch' it.

There *is* an element of sheer misfortune in postnatal depression and people with it can certainly be desperately ill, especially if they have the more severe forms, but I would never want to ignore the clear social, psychological and emotional factors in its development.

Motherhood is complex, strange and only partly understood. It's an experience, yet it's also a state of being. Once pregnant, we have changed – forever. I think the work of people like Rozsika Parker and Joan Raphael-Leff (see Bibliography) who deliver new insights from a more 'woman-friendly' form of psychoanalysis and psychology to the study of mothering, will bring a greater understanding of post-natal depression, and help us see why some women are more likely to experience it. The idea that postnatal depression can be a creative, protective and even a necessary response to emotional and social factors was a new one to me.

I have drawn a distinction, based on current clinical consensus, between postnatal depression and puerperal psychosis, and devoted a separate chapter to the latter.

So many people have helped me with this book.

Apart from my journalist/writer background in women's health and family issues, which has brought me many contacts with women and health professionals, I have interviewed at length fifteen women (and one man) about their own experiences. I can't name them, as confidentiality was agreed as a condition. My thanks to them.

Thanks also to NCT's Sue Orchard, and to *New Generation*, the NCT's own journal. (Now I know why I have never thrown a copy away – here was a brilliant source of thoughtful, insightful and honest personal experiences going back twenty years.) I have continued to show up at meetings and conferences about postnatal depression; it's notable that a broad range of health and social work professionals now feel that support for new mothers is within their remit to offer.

I am delighted that the Community Practitioners' and Health Visitors' Association are making this second edition a joint venture with NCT. Health visitors have been in the vanguard of practical, effective support and treatment of women with postnatal depression. Cheryll Adams, from the CPHVA's office for research and practice development and Briege Coyle, Professional Officer, CPHVA Northern Ireland, both made very valuable suggestions and amendments in this new edition.

I have been fortunate enough not to have experienced postnatal depression myself. I am full of admiration for the women who have, and who have recovered – and women do, nearly always, recover – and who want to spread the word about it, to show there's no need for fear, or guilt, or shame. We need women like them.

Heather Welford
May 2002

Author's note: all unannotated quotations in the book come from the 15 women (and one man) I interviewed. I have left them unattributed, as a means of maintaining their confidentiality. The case histories in Chapter 5 have named protagonists, but all the names have been changed.

Have I got Postnatal Depression?

'I wanted someone to look after me...'

After she had her baby, Wendy felt she was inside a 'bottomless pit'. She saw no way out.

'Friends and family try to instil hope into your empty soul,' she says now. 'They do their best, saying, "you will feel better, it just takes time". What else can they say? The alternative would be too awful to imagine. But you don't believe them. You can't.'[1]

For a substantial number of women, the weeks and months around childbirth are marked by the unhappiness and negative feelings we call postnatal depression.

Just how substantial that number is, is not clear. Textbooks on the topic generally quote studies which put it at between 10 and 15 per cent of all new mothers.[2] However, other studies reveal higher totals of as much as 27 per cent.[3] If you include in your definition of post-natal depression all post-childbirth distress and misery, including the more shortlived forms, it's probable the majority of mothers recognize many of the symptoms from their own personal experience.

However, a practical definition of postnatal depression is that it's a depressed mood which lasts, which overwhelms more positive feelings, and which becomes evident in the first weeks and months after childbirth.

Like Other Depressions?

Some medical research and writing holds that depression after childbirth 'feels' like depression at any other time of life:

'Postnatal depression is like other kinds of depression, except that it is brought on by having a baby,' as MIND's leaflet on the topic says.

There is another view, though, that postnatal depression has a different symptom profile compared to other forms of depression. Katharina Dalton, a doctor who has worked with many women who have had postnatal depression, says in her book *Depression after Childbirth* (Oxford University Press, 1996), 'irritability and violence are also possible symptoms... and because they rarely appear in depression outside the postnatal period, postnatal depression is experienced as a distinct condition'.

It may even be that women are no more at risk of developing depression after childbirth than at other stressful times in their lives. Researcher Sarah Clement, speaking at a major conference held on the topic in 1996, raised this possibility – and it surfaces now and again in other work as well. Until we get a more consistent definition of postnatal depression and a greater understanding of the biological, emotional, social and psychiatric elements of it, we can't be sure.

However, there is contradictory evidence that childbirth is an especially vulnerable time for women and mental health; for example, in one study women were shown to be three times more likely to devel op depression in the weeks following childbirth than at any other time.[4] Moreover, as Sarah Clement points out, depression at this particular time may be more difficult for a woman than at any other time, because of the exceptional demands being made upon her as a new mother.

The Different Forms of Postnatal Distress

Postnatal distress affects mothers in one or more of three basic ways.

1. The 'Blues'

The first, and most common, is simply known as the 'blues', some-times defined as the 'maternity blues', 'postnatal blues', 'three–day blues' or 'baby blues'. Surprisingly, nobody has yet got their Latin or Greek dictionaries on the term to make it sound any more highfalutin' or 'medical'. It's also called 'third-day blues' or 'fourth-day blues' because it commonly strikes on these days after the birth.

It affects at least half of all new mothers, at some point in the first week after the birth. The main sign of it is tearfulness, and a feeling of coming down to earth with a bump.

'On day two I was amazingly pleased with myself at having gone through the birth, producing a beautiful baby. Then on day three the feeding went awry, the baby got a spotty face, my husband was half an hour later than he said he'd be, and my mother said something I thought was stupid on the phone.

I cried and cried – pinning the reason for my tears on all the things that had gone wrong, but I knew none of them deserved my over-the-top reaction. I felt touchy and self-pitying, and scared about how I'd cope in the months ahead. Then, the next day I went home and I was okay.'

The blues are so common, and so often lift by themselves, it's speculated that it's a physiological – that is, a biological and normal – response to the hormonal after-effects of having a baby. As one obstetrician says, 'the blues are well-recognized as an almost normal reaction to the earlier elation.'[5]

Precisely why the upsurge of prolactin (the milk-making hormone) should have this effect is not clear. However, all of us have experienced the way any major and life-changing set of events, positive or negative, can sometimes cause tearfulness and confusion as the immediate impact wears off – it's part of being human.

After all, pregnancy and childbirth are certainly major and life-changing events; for many of us, having a baby is just about the most important thing that happens to us. It would be far more surprising if none of us was affected by the blues, especially when most of us have to come to terms with these events in an unfamiliar environment (the maternity unit), and among strangers (other mothers, hospital staff).

I have heard midwives say that postnatal blues are less likely to happen after a home birth. It would be difficult to show this convincingly. Women who choose home birth in the UK are a self-selected group, and may be less susceptible to the blues for some other reason, connected to their personality and outlook, rather than the setting in which they give birth. A Dutch study showed there was no difference in the incidence of blues between home and hospital birth. But home birth in Holland (at between a third and half of all deliveries) is far more mainstream than in the UK. We can't transfer the results to British women.[6]

Postnatal blues doesn't need any treatment, other than a supportive and sympathetic approach from the people caring for the mother.

Do the Blues Lead to Postnatal Depression?

It's true that women who experience the blues appear to be more likely to suffer from postnatal depression as time goes on, but the association seems most strongly marked in severe cases.[7] Most cases of the blues don't develop into postnatal depression. The blues seems to be a quite separate phenomenon. There is, for example, usually a time lapse between the end of the blues and the start of postnatal depression. Symptoms of postnatal depression are experienced as deeper, more pervasive and they are certainly longer-lasting.

2. Postnatal Depression

The second form of distress – and the one that will take up the greater part of the discussion in this book – is the form that we tend to know, indeed, as postnatal depression.

Clinicians diagnose postnatal depression if it shows itself in the weeks or months after childbirth, but this may not be when it begins.

Many of the women I have spoken to trace the start of their feelings to pregnancy, and there are numerous anecdotal accounts of pregnancy or antenatal depression in journals such as *New Generation*. An increasing body of research is discovering, even 'proving', that it exists, too.

It certainly seems that the more women's own experiences are studied in detail, the more it appears that while women's symptoms of depression may be reported after childbirth, and they become more obvious to those around them at that time, they may have their origins months earlier.

Research Studies

One major study which looked at 9,000 mothers[8] found that depression was actually more likely in pregnancy compared to afterwards, and the rate of depression tended to decline following childbirth. Depression in pregnancy tends to be overlooked, say the researchers, as any mood changes are ascribed to the underlying effects of pregnancy.[9]

A smaller study ended up calling the depression they found 'perinatal depression', which refers to depression around the time of childbirth. The study revealed that 13.7 per cent were depressed at 36 weeks of pregnancy.[10]

Being depressed in pregnancy is in any case a clear risk factor for developing postnatal depression (see page 22), though being depressed in pregnancy doesn't mean you will be the same postnatally.

We need to know a lot more about the links between pregnancy depression and postnatal depression. How often, for example, is it the same depression, punctuated by a brief respite immediately after the birth? How often is it a different depression, with a separate beginning that arises postnatally? It's clear that more research is needed.

What Are the Signs of Postnatal Depression?

Whatever the precise timing of postnatal depression, it has a wide range of symptoms, and it varies in its severity. Some women are virtually disabled by it, unable to care for themselves or their baby, while still being in touch with reality (unlike the symptoms of puerperal psychosis, see page 121 and elsewhere). Other women's symptoms are not so overwhelming, and they manage to struggle along, even hiding how they feel from their friends and family.

There's a broad spectrum, and it may be that symptoms differ in intensity according to the level of support a woman has, how easy or how difficult her baby is to care for, and factors such as her physical health and strength.

A mother may show, express or experience:

- ❑ lethargy
- ❑ tearfulness
- ❑ anxiety
- ❑ guilt
- ❑ irritability
- ❑ confusion
- ❑ disturbed sleep
- ❑ excessive exhaustion
- ❑ difficulties making decisions
- ❑ loss of self-esteem
- ❑ lack of confidence in her ability as a mother
- ❑ no enjoyment of motherhood
- ❑ fear of harming herself or the baby
- ❑ loss of libido
- ❑ loss of appetite
- ❑ hostility or indifference to people she normally loves
- ❑ difficulty in concentrating
- ❑ shame at being unable to be happy
- ❑ fear of judgement
- ❑ helplessness

Few women will experience all of these symptoms at any one time, or even over the whole time they are depressed. It's important to note, too, that just about all new mothers will feel tired and lacking in confidence and energy, and experience guilt and anxiety to some degree.

But a depressed mother feels very little joy and delight in the baby, and in motherhood. Her negative feelings predominate. We will see (pages 40–41) that for some authors and researchers, a lack of joy and delight is a normal and understandable response to motherhood, and that what clinicians term depression is in fact good old (or bad old) misery and unhappiness, writ large.

Negative Feelings

Some examples of these negative feelings include the ones expressed by a mother who spoke to writer Rozsika Parker for her book *Torn in Two* (Virago, 1995):

> 'She wasn't a particularly difficult baby. I just never felt I knew what the matter was. I didn't think I felt hostile towards her. I turned it against myself. It was my failure to understand what was needed; my inability to cope. In a way it was easier to blame myself and to think of it in those terms, although it made me terribly helpless.'

Other examples from interviews:

> 'I felt so irritated and irritable – I was not a very nice person. I couldn't understand it. I'd say to myself "you've got what you wanted – why aren't you satisfied?"'

> 'I felt so lonely, and I blamed my husband for so much. I found NCT to be a lifeline. They were the only ones who acknowledged that life with a baby is very hard.'

> 'There were days when I truly felt like smothering the children and taking an overdose myself – not every day was as bad, and I recognized the fact that deep down I didn't want to go as far as this. I managed to cope – it actually helped that I had to go to school with my older child, and collect him at the

end of the day. I couldn't do much else apart from that – it felt like too much hassle to arrange any outings.'

Psychiatrist Jane Price spoke to a mother with a powerful sense of loss of self, in her book *Motherhood: What It Does to Your Mind* (Pandora, 1988):

'I felt as if I was falling into a hole much like Alice in Wonderland. Nothing made sense any more. I was not the boss, had no control, could make no decisions, and every second seemed full of something or somebody else apart from me. Within two weeks I had lost any sense of who or what I had ever been and I began to feel as if I had died. My tears were a form of grief at losing the "me" I was familiar with.'

3. Puerperal Psychosis

The third form of depression after childbirth isn't anything like the usual clinically defined phenomenon of depression. It is puerperal psychosis. Translated into laywoman's terms, this is a madness (psychosis) that strikes in the weeks after childbirth (the period known as the puerperium).

I once had a letter from a woman who told me she had suffered a 'purple' psychosis, and the image that small error inspires seems an accurate picture of this distressing and frightening syndrome.

Puerperal psychosis affects between one and two new mothers in every 1,000. Unlike postnatal depression, it is usually clear to anyone who comes in contact with the mother that she is suffering from a mental disturbance. It begins soon after childbirth – sometimes in the very first days. The mother cannot hide it, even if she wanted to, and she usually experiences delusions and distortions of reality.

However, there is a range of symptoms, according to the type of psychosis. Some women hallucinate – they see objects or people who aren't there, or bright colours and patterns swirl in front of them. Some mothers seem to suffer a form of manic depression, or bi-polar illness, though with clinical features that are perhaps more dramatic and distressing. When the sufferer is high, she is abnormally energetic and excited; when she is low, she can barely talk. A third form is an extremely severe form of depression, without any highs or shows of energy, and possibly with persistent dark and self-hating thoughts.

Puerperal psychosis always needs medical treatment and almost always admission to hospital.

Puerperal psychosis is discussed in more detail in Chapter 7.

The Missing Voices
– We Need to Listen to Women

The experience of postnatal depression is unique to each woman: while one woman's depression may share similar features to another's, there will be other aspects which are quite different. Some women's depression is more severe, and longer-lasting, though recovery times vary a great deal (see pages 68-70). For an estimated one or two in every 10, the depression lasts for a year or more.[11]

It's obvious that we can only know of this diversity for sure by talking to women themselves. Yet surprisingly, not much research has been devoted to finding out what postnatal depression really 'feels' like. Much of this book will record some of those feelings, to catch some of the missing voices, to record something of what it is to experience this phenomenon.

We'll also hear about the circumstances that surround and precede the feelings, and whether and how these circumstances relate to the feelings.

These are voices of just some of the thousands upon thousands of women who have found themselves, let's say, struggling to 'cope' during and/or before the first months of motherhood with the responsibility for the daily physical and emotional care of others – very small, very dependent and very demanding others – as well as themselves. That struggle to cope is in itself lonely, and it can lead to further isolation.

Moreover, the struggle doesn't always succeed. Sometimes, even when it does, there may be a price to pay – a broken marriage, a thwarted career, a change (for the worse) of outlook when a naturally cheerful personality becomes dulled and negative. And often, it's a hidden struggle, a struggle the woman herself may feel is shameful and which sets her apart from others, who she feels are all managing wonderfully well – leaving her feeling as if she's failed.

'I've lost count the number of times I rang my husband to come home early from work as I really feared I would batter the baby. I had already shaken him and thrown him into his cot out of sheer frustration and anger ... it needed monumental effort to get him ready to go out in his pram. The most overwhelming feeling was one of total failure. I felt totally inadequate as a mother – me, who'd been a competent teacher, yet now couldn't even cope with one baby. Coupled with all this was the shame I felt – even after I was having medical treatment. I got sick of being told "pull yourself together". That's just what you *can't* do.'

'After four months, I felt I couldn't go on. I rang my health visitor and she was so surprised to hear me say I couldn't cope … all she'd seen was the way I could go out and about as if there was nothing wrong. I put my lipstick and a smiley face on like a mask.'

'I was tearful, and resentful of the baby. I couldn't hear sad things on the news without crying. I was shy and quiet – not like the other mums at NCT meetings. They all seemed so bright and cheerful and capable.'

'I felt desperate, distraught … I went to live at my mum's house, and it was a bit better. I didn't have to do anything. I could just sit and be a blob if I wanted to … and I did want to.'

'She was born in the September – and I remember that following winter as a great, slow, worsening gloom.'

'The trouble with going to things like the National Childbirth Trust is you meet the perfect mums there and I just used to come home feeling more inadequate. They were obviously very content with motherhood and childrearing.'

'I hated myself. I hated everything about myself. I felt useless. I felt so sure everything I was doing was wrong.'

'I was so desperately tired, but I couldn't sleep. I had no feelings of love towards Amy. I was actually bored, and lonely, too. Yet at the same time I was terrified Amy would be taken away from me. At times I was tearful, and at other times I was full of rage.'

'Being a mother came as a nasty shock. I didn't want to know.

When my mother came to stay I was so glad I could get her to take the baby off my hands. I felt like a child myself towards the baby – I sometimes said to her "why don't you go away you horrible little thing?"'

'Everything had gone so well with my first baby. I never expected things to be so different. I just hated him. I actually called my parents, and left a message saying I didn't want him in the house. But I felt guilty and inadequate, and at some level I knew my behaviour was bizarre and I was so exasperated with other people – why could they not see I was odd?'

'I worried about everything. I was sick with anxiety, literally sick – real vomiting. I wanted to sleep all the time, but sleep didn't do anything for me. I never felt as if I'd had a refreshing rest.'

'I had thought the baby would bring me fulfilment and pleasure; she didn't. I was bored, disappointed and desperate to escape, but I had resigned from my job and so I considered I had ruined my life by having her.'

'I'm never alone but I am very lonely and lost. There's something missing but I don't know what it is.'

Fiona Shaw's autobiographical account of postnatal depression, *Out of Me* (Viking, 1997) describes a powerful sense of isolation: 'When people suggested to me that I had no good reason for being so full of self-disgust, their words made no sense. I was torpid, a sham. I deserved no self-respect. Most of the time I was terribly alone, lost, in a harsh and far-away place, a horrible terrain, reserved for me alone.'

Depressed Responses

Cheryl Tatano Beck looked at the way postnatally depressed mothers reacted to their children, for *Nursing Research* (March/April 1996). The following three experiences come from her work:

'Every time my baby cried when she woke up, I'd feel a chill go up my body and I wanted her to stay asleep because I knew it was so hard when she woke up. I remember the fear of the baby needing me, or crying for my help ...'

'I had no control of my own self-being – nothing ... mind, soul, nothing. It basically controlled me. I wanted to reach out to my baby, but couldn't.'

'The fact that I couldn't love her normally made the guilt even worse. You just don't feel anything good for your baby. You just feel full of guilt. One night I actually remember walking in the room, and looking at her sleeping in the crib. I was crying because I felt so bad for her that I was her mother.'

Darcy Haapala wrote about her depression in *Midwifery Today* (Summer 1995), which began three weeks after the birth of her second baby. 'I was burdened by a tremendous sense of guilt and shame. That innate mother instinct I had felt so much with my first child was replaced with an agonizing self-absorption and lack of feeling for my new baby.'

Questions and Answers

Q. IS POSTNATAL DEPRESSION A MODERN EXPERIENCE? MY MOTHER
SAYS IT WAS NEVER HEARD OF IN HER DAY. AND DO WOMEN IN
OTHER CULTURES SUFFER FROM POSTNATAL DEPRESSION?

A. Old medical textbooks refer to mental illness after childbirth, sometimes known as 'lactational insanity', but the term postnatal depression is only about 35 years old, with the first real study of it with that name coming out in 1968.[12] That does not mean it didn't exist, but it may not have been recognized.

It's not really known if women in other cultures experience postnatal depression. Mental health and illness are rooted in the cultural and social experience. It's difficult to compare symptoms, too, due to differences in outlook and language problems.

Some anthropologists contend that postnatal depression, as Western women know it, is a Western phenomenon. There is evidence that women from other cultures who come to the West may be at equal risk from postnatal depression, however, but it may be more difficult to express a need for help, and for appropriate treatment and support to be given.[13]

Q. CAN POSTNATAL DEPRESSION BE AVOIDED OR PREVENTED?

A. There are claims that giving progesterone therapy (see page 33) can prevent women becoming depressed a second time, but these claims await evaluation.

Some drugs, for example Lithium, may be successful in preventing a repeat episode of puerperal psychosis, and research (at the University of Birmingham) is examining this possibility.[14]

There is some evidence that giving women extra social support in pregnancy – via devices such as support groups, or extra health visitor or midwife visits for listening – can reduce the chances of the women in the 'target group' getting postnatal depression. Sarah Clement has written about listening visits in pregnancy (in *Midwifery*, January 1995), which seem to increase new mothers' emotional well-being, but the research on 'targeting' social support to actively prevent postnatal depression is still, I think, unconvincing. Some mothers have been given the opportunity to 'debrief' their childbirth experience with a midwife, find out answers to questions and express their feelings about how the birth went. Schemes like this have not yet been shown to make any difference, though. We still need programmes that are easily reproducible in any area, and which can be delivered by community health professionals, and which are easy to evaluate.

References for Chapter One

1 W. Hawthorne. Surviving postnatal depression. *Health Visitor*, December 1997.

2 For example, J.L. Cox (ed). *Transcultural Psychiatry*, Croom Helm, 1986.

3 C.G. Ballard *et al*. Prevalence of postnatal psychiatric morbidity in mothers and fathers. *British Journal of Psychiatry*, June 1994.

4 J.L. Cox, G. Chapman. A controlled study of the onset, duration and prevalence of postnatal depression. *British Journal of Psychiatry*, Vol. 163, 27–31, 1993.

5 R. Neuberg. *Obstetrics: A Practical Manual*, Oxford Medical Publications, 1995.

6 V.J. Pop *et al*. Blues and depression during early puerperium: home versus hospital deliveries. *British Journal of Obstetrics and Gynaecology*, September 1995.

7 P. Hannah *et al.* Links between early postpartum mood and post-natal depression. *British Journal of Psychiatry*, June 1992.

8 D.M. Fergusson *et al.* Changes in depression during and following pregnancy. *Paediatric and Perinatal Epidemiology*, Vol. 10, 279–93, 1996.

9 *ibid.*

10 V. Levy, P. Kline. Perinatal depression: a factor analysis. *British Journal of Midwifery*, April 1994.

11 C. Kumar. Postnatal depression. *New Generation*, December 1987.

12 B. Pitt, 'Atypical' depression following childbirth. *British Journal of Psychiatry*, 114:1325–35, 1968.

13 K. Thompson. Detecting postnatal depression in Asian women. *Health Visitor*, June 1997.

14 Action on Puerperal Psychosis Newsletter, April 2002.

2

What Causes Depression
after Childbirth?

'Expectations flooded in from everywhere ...'

It's just not known for sure what causes postnatal depression –
though there are plenty of ideas about it. As one psychologist says,
'the symptoms of postnatal depression [present] a confused picture
of what postnatal depression actually is. It is hardly surprising, therefore, that the causes of [it] have also proved difficult to identify.'[1]

There are a number of factors that have been examined or suggested as 'causes'. Lots of the research has looked at which women
experience postnatal depression, and what their lives, their back-
grounds, their families, their circumstances, have in common.

Armed with this knowledge, it's thought that health professionals
might be able to predict postnatal depression, and (it's assumed) offer
effective help more quickly. It could be useful to women themselves,
too, goes the theory, as it may encourage them to be conscious of
symptoms and to take them seriously, if they think they could be more
likely to be at risk. Looking for these 'risk factors' could, it's suggested,
also help increase the general understanding of the experience.

Is 'Increased Risk' a Cause?

Some research applies the term 'causative' to risk factors, implying that we know that certain events or physical or psychological phenomena actually cause postnatal depression. I don't yet think we can be sure enough that anything, especially social and emotional factors, actually cause postnatal depression.

Causes and effects are tricky creatures. It wouldn't be strictly correct to say that running across the road is going to cause you to be run over by the 38 bus – because when all's said and done, it's the bus that's involved in the collision. However, running across the road puts you into a situation whereby an accident is more likely to happen. If you run across the road at the time you know the 38 bus is timetabled to appear, then you increase your risk ... but it's still not the real cause of your accident.

This isn't quite the same as postnatal depression, though. Postnatal depression is not 'out there' like a 38 bus, trundling along, waiting to 'get' you if you are unlucky enough, or daft enough, to encounter it in the middle of the High Street. It doesn't come round the corner in a rush. Instead, it arises from within a woman's experience, whether that experience emerges from her biology, her background, or the social situation she's in as a mother at the beginning of the 21st century. Maybe causes of postnatal depression will turn out to be a pick 'n' mix of many elements, with the mother in the wrong place at the wrong time, feeling as if she's at the centre of a collision of circumstances.

Even so, we still make a leap when we say any of these experiences cause postnatal depression, rather than that they are strongly linked or associated with it. And even if we do make the leap, and attribute the cause of postnatal depression to one or more risk factors, we could only ever reach a partial explanation.

Having a whole pramload of risk factors doesn't mean postnatal depression is inevitable – plenty of women who look on paper as though they'd be prime candidates for it don't experience it. Other women, with no apparent risk factors, *do* suffer – though there is often something that the women themselves recognize as causing stress or unhappiness. We just don't know why some women succumb, and others don't.

What Increases Your Risk of Postnatal Depression?

The factors associated with the development of postnatal depression, based on a reading of much of the recent work done on the issue, include:

- ❑ severe baby blues (see pages 3-5) – an attack of the blues which doesn't pass quickly or which is perceived by the mother or her carers as being especially intense and distressing.[2]
- ❑ an experience of the 'highs' immediately after the birth. The highs are feelings of euphoria, lack of a need to sleep, feelings of extra energy and difficulty in concentrating. About 10 per cent of women experience the highs, and they are at greater risk of developing postnatal depression later.[3]
- ❑ the lack of a confidante – someone to talk to, a 'best friend' or supporter from whatever part of your life or work. It seems feeling someone is listening to you is important to protect you from postnatal depression.[4]
- ❑ a poor relationship with one's partner.[5]
- ❑ poor emotional support in pregnancy from your own mother and

father and the midwife, and poor practical support in pregnancy from the midwife.[6]

- a lot of support – emotional and practical – in pregnancy from one's partner.[7] See below for more on this surprising finding.
- having an unhelpful partner – that is, one who doesn't share in household tasks.[8]
- depression in pregnancy. Research has suggested women could be asked about their feelings of depression in pregnancy via an appropriate questionnaire designed to find out which women might need psychiatric or other professional help, because the link between antenatal depression and postnatal depression in some studies is strong.[9]
- women who have a previous or family history of depression.[10]
- women who have some intervention in childbirth (for example, forceps) and who have a history of 'psychiatric vulnerability' – of itself, having a complicated birth does not constitute a risk factor, but it does appear that this coupled with previous mental distress or illness can 'tip' some women into postnatal depression.[11]
- women who have an emergency caesarean section are at greater risk than mothers having a forceps or normal delivery. In fact they are six times more likely to be postnatally depressed at three months after the birth.[12]
- women who didn't feel in control of events during labour may have low emotional well-being scores when assessed six weeks after the birth.[13]
- negative life events after the birth, which would include the death of a close relative or marital problems.[14]
- difficult social and/or economic circumstances.[15]
- irritable baby who is demanding and cries a lot. It's surprising, but the role of the baby in postnatal depression has hardly been looked at until recently – as if babies are (a) all the same as each other and (b) have no influence themselves on the mother's feelings.

Of course, a depressed mother may affect the baby's behaviour (see pages 105–8), and a crying baby may be that way because of his mother's depression. We need to allow for that before we can suggest that it's the baby influencing the mother – in other words, the demandingness and the crying has to come before the depression.

This was done with a sample of mothers in Cambridge, and Professor Lynne Murray, who coordinated the research and reported on it in *Health Visitor* (September 1997), found that in cases where the baby's motor control was poor (this refers to the baby's reflex responses and head and limb control), and where the baby was irritable, the mother's risk of depression increased significantly.

Other Factors

In addition, some studies have drawn a link between social and emotional factors such as poor childhood relationships, the loss of a parent, and a poor relationship with one's own mother (though see page 35).

Disillusionment

There is also the idea of 'disappointed expectations' which I have heard expressed casually by obstetricians and midwives, usually when criticizing antenatal classes or birth plans.

One academic paper put it like this '... many expectant parents have come to see childbirth as some sort of transcendental experience in which every detail must accord with their preordained, idealised notions. That childbirth experiences can often fall short of such exaggerated expectations is a potent source of disappointment and sense of loss for such parents.'[16]

Antenatal classes are sometimes blamed by health professionals for raising women's expectations, causing them disappointment and guilt when the reality fails to match up.

Yet I think this view tells us a lot about the difficulty some health professionals still have about mother's choices in childbirth and their right to be involved in decisions about maternity care. It says very little about postnatal depression. I have met parents who have clear hopes for the birth, and those who wish their birth had gone differently, for many reasons (one of those reasons might be the way their professional carers disregarded their expressed wishes). But the picture painted of 'many' parents suffering depression because they missed out on a detailed 'transcendental experience', whatever that is, is one I don't recognize. Mothers who feel failures at having pain relief may have strong views about non-intervention, but good antenatal teachers are normally keen to extend choice and to support the role of the mother at the centre of decision-making. They do their best to counter tendencies for the mother to blame herself if birth is less than straightforward or if she decides she wants pain relief.

Feeling disappointed and disillusioned with motherhood, though, is indeed a potent source of distress for many women, and ties in with Professor Murray's research about 'difficult' babies predisposing their mothers to postnatal depression. Feeling your baby's needs or your own 'performance' as a mother don't begin to match up with the dreams you had, is part of the package of negative emotions that come with feeling depressed.

Sometimes They Say One Thing ... Sometimes Another

The literature on the risk factors of postnatal depression is sometimes contradictory; some studies discover some factors are far stronger than others, while other studies find no difference. This apparent confusion is partly to do with the way postnatal depression is defined in studies, and the differences that there may be between postnatal depression that begins within the first few weeks, and postnatal depression that begins later than this.

Research doesn't always ask the same questions in the same way, either. For example, in one of the studies listed above, women in the survey were only at risk of postnatal depression if they had a caesarean section plus a history of mental illness. Caesarean section – both types, that is, emergency and planned – was lumped in with forceps as an 'obstetric intervention'. In another study, an emergency caesarean section was a risk factor on its own. But in this second study, women were not asked about their previous psychiatric history. Results might have been different if they were – we just don't know.

Other studies measure things like 'emotional well-being' or 'mood'. The timing of the questioning may differ – you may get a different set of answers if you ask the same mother what she's feeling at five days, five weeks or five months.

A Supportive Partner?

Sometimes, though, things truly aren't as contradictory as they appear. Unexpected findings can be justified. Sandra Wheatley's study on partner's support (*op.cit.*) found that mothers who described their partners as giving a *lot* of support to them while they were pregnant were more likely to be depressed postnatally than mothers whose partners were *not* supportive.

Now this is surprising. Surely we take it for granted that a supportive partner is important in pregnancy to prevent negative feelings, whether or not we define them as postnatal depression?

The finding was startling enough to be picked up by the newspapers in 1997, when Wheatley's research paper was presented to a meeting of the British Association for the Advancement of Science. It created quite a stir.

At first glance, it looked like the 'new man' was the cause of postnatal depression. Was this not an odd finding, came the question? Yes, especially when in the same study, pregnancy support from other sources was shown to be less likely to be linked with postnatal depression.

Yet Wheatley has an explanation that I think goes some way at least to removing the apparent contradiction. Her view is that women with supportive partners felt they had accumulated 'caring debts' they felt they could not repay – and that added to their stress. Put it this way – your partner is absolutely marvellous when you're pregnant. Bless him, he does the shopping, cooks the meals, reads the books with you and learns about massage and breathing so he can help you in labour. He loves you, and shows it, and, like you, he looks forward to being a parent, talking about all the wonderful things you're both going to do with the baby. All right ... he's a so-called 'new man' in newspaperspeak. Then reality sets in with the birth: you feel tired and stressed and unsexy and disillusioned. His clear disappointment at everything in the garden not being lovely makes you feel guilty when you remember what a hero he's been to you. You end up even more stressed – and more likely to be depressed.

A Chosen Sample

It's also worth noting that some studies which say they identify risk factors rely on quite small samples of mothers. This is inevitable in research. The questionnaires and interviews needed to elicit information about feelings and experiences can be very time-consuming. A postnatal depression study can't just take hospital records off a computer and sort them, in the way some projects do, number-crunching them into reports about medical treatments or type of delivery. A survey of feelings involves a lot of one-to-one encounters between researchers and mothers – and often, a lot of work after-wards to interpret the results. So surveys of mothers may be very good for what the experts call qualitative research, when we're finding out about human experiences in detail. But they may be less reliable in quantitative research, when we're looking at statistics and likelihoods and numbers.

Let's take the Wheatley survey, which found that 'new men' increased the risk of depression as an example. It involved just 48 women, only 12 of whom were depressed. Yet in social science research terms that's a respectable number. I have seen surveys of mothers looking at many aspects of their experience and care which have involved less than 10. There are statistical techniques that allow for a smallish sample, and enable you to calculate how likely it is that your findings are mere chance, or are truly significant. Despite her small numbers, Wheatley's findings stand up as being potentially significant – though she herself declines to draw dogmatic conclusions from them, and simply says she 'strongly advocates' further investigation into the influence of partners.

Progress in predicting postnatal depression is hampered by two important facts: first, the relative smallness of the samples that have uncovered these risk factors, and secondly, the way even the most strongly predictive factors – lack of social support and a previous history of depression – don't 'guarantee' the development of postnatal depression. Far from it. Professor Murray and colleagues, reporting in *Archives of Disease in Childhood* in 1997, found that even when tests have been done based on seeing which women have the most risk factors, they could predict only half of all cases of postnatal depression correctly.

Mothers Talk About Their Lives
Before Depression

Mothers often have an insight into what they believe has contributed to the reason why they got depression at this particular time. It's true that puerperal psychosis can sometimes appear as a 'bolt from the blue', though even then, when mothers look back they can often remember disorientation or other symptoms before it truly took off. However, the bulk of this book is taken up with the experience of postnatal depression that's not psychotic – and this type of depression tends not to descend suddenly and inexplicably like a rain cloud on a bright summer's day. Mothers frequently recognize 'bad weather' on the horizon.

One study puts it this way: 'for the most part, women's own explanations of their depression lie firmly within the context of their lives as mothers.'[17] The same study listed factors that mothers they had surveyed put forward as significant. In order, they were:

❑ feeling unsupported
❑ being isolated
❑ exhaustion
❑ physical health factors
❑ lack of time or space for oneself
❑ material circumstances
❑ illness or death of a loved one
❑ baby temperament
❑ hormones or biology
❑ tendency to depression.

There was also a wide range of other factors named by individual women, showing, according to the authors, 'much diversity in women's accounts'.

Here's what some of the women I talked to told me:

'I had very little support from midwives when I got home – it was Christmas, staff was short, and I felt as if I'd been left alone. It wasn't an ideal time for asking for any help. Years before I had children I suffered from depression, which was helped with psychotherapy. I knew what it felt like – and I recognized the signs.'

'I had a dreadful pregnancy – I was in a car accident when I was six months, and ended up in a wheelchair at seven months. I had a 48-hour labour which was so badly managed by staff. I had three epidurals, none of which worked. There was no support from the hospital staff, and they didn't seem to know what they were doing. It was a holiday weekend, and that affected staffing levels. I was told to push, and then not to push, for five hours. Afterwards, no one took any responsibility for what happened to me, though it was obvious I hadn't been treated well.'

'It took me three years to conceive, and in the end I was planning on going for IVF, when at last I became pregnant. I was delighted, but by the end of the pregnancy I was extremely anxious. I ended up with a caesarean under general anaesthetic after a failed induction – it was horrendous. I just didn't feel as if I was in control of my labour at all. Afterwards I was just wiped out. The whole birth experience was so upsetting. Then, the next day my father had a massive heart attack and was rushed into hospital.'

'The birth was an emergency caesarean after a very painful induction. I was so bitter – I kept thinking of all the pulling around that had been done to me.'

'The pregnancy and birth were great – I'd planned a home birth but ended up being induced as she was a fortnight over-due. The staff explained everything, though, and I felt great. But when I got home, I was more or less on my own as my husband works away a lot. My family were nowhere near. The baby didn't sleep much, and I had no friends. I was so lonely.'

'We have a family history of depression, but this was the first time it had hit me. The baby was not easy. She was so noisy – she screamed and screamed and screamed. My husband had just lost his job, and his mother fell seriously ill.'

And a published personal experience, from the Association of Postnatal Illness newsletter in 1996: 'When I was pregnant, I was working as a horticulturalist at a local park. One of my colleagues played a joke on me that went wrong. He was driving a tractor and the bucket of it pinned me up against some wooden spikes. I had to go to hospital and although the baby was unhurt, there was a big enquiry and the whole experience marked the start of my depression. I worried all the time.'

Post-traumatic Shock After Birth

Some women experience a form of psychiatric disorder after birth known as post-traumatic shock disorder, or PTSD. This is the phenomenon which received a lot of press coverage after it was diagnosed as experienced by people who witnessed the tragedy at Hillsborough football ground, or people who had been held as hostages. It may also be diagnosed after less public but no less distressing events for the individual, such as a road accident, or a rape.

PTSD has been officially recognized since 1980 by the American Psychiatric Association as applying to anyone fitting the half-dozen diagnostic criteria which differentiate it from 'straight' depression or temporary shock. One criterion is, for example, that the person must continue to re-experience the damaging event in some way through nightmares or flashbacks; another is that the person must have experienced fear for his/her life or bodily integrity, or that of a loved one; yet another is that the person deliberately avoids being reminded of the experience, or else develops a sort of general emotional numbness.

When PTSD happens after childbirth, it's been termed 'birth trauma'. One textbook estimates that seven per cent of women suffer it after birth,[18] though it may never be diagnosed as this, and the symptoms may overlap with those of depression. PTSD is sometimes characterised by 'pathological complaining' and violent thoughts about the staff held responsible. One mother who had a bad birth experience regularly telephoned her local maternity unit, sometimes late at night, to berate the staff. Another confessed to wanting to beat the midwife to a pulp.[19]

The trauma experienced by these women is focused on their labour. It may be caused by a lack of support in labour; severe pain and/or fear; long length of labour; poor or insensitive or even rough treatment in labour; sudden or poorly understood interventions.

The framework for it appears to be made up of one or more of four experiences:

❑ physical trauma (ranging from caesarean section to episiotomy) which may be perceived by the mother as damage
❑ stigmatization, when the mother feels blemished in some way by

the birth experience, and which might include the baby being taken to the special care unit, as well as some residual physical sign of recent labour

❑ betrayal, when the mother feels let down or abused by her carers
❑ powerlessness, when the mother feels a loss of control.[20]

Nursing Times, in March 1994, reported the case of a mother who suffered a long and gruelling labour followed by an emergency caesarean section. 'Even when her child slept she could not rest. Her thoughts were constantly invaded by video-like replays of events during her labour ... she was continually searching for what she could have said or done to have changed things. She could picture the midwife and hear the words that had hurt her so much: "You can't help it if you can't cope." She was plagued with guilt that she had lost self-control and with the memory of the fear that she and her child might have died.'

AIMS, the Association for Improvements in the Maternity Services, ran this account in their journal of Summer 1997: '[The doctor] then proceeded with the most brutally forceful internal it has ever been my terror to experience. Despite crying out in pain and writhing on the narrow bed, he continued with his jabbing exploration ... I felt as though I had been raped.' This woman experienced very poor, unsympathetic and sometimes frightening care antenatally and during the birth, and was diagnosed with PTSD as a direct result of it. She brought charges against the hospital for assault and substandard care and was eventually awarded £11,000 in damages.

PTSD can be helped with psychotherapy and counselling, and about half of all sufferers recover within three months.[21]

Many cases of PTSD should be avoidable in the first place – there is no excuse for treating women so badly in labour they feel assaulted and invaded. Health professionals have a vital role here.

An early opportunity to debrief birth by talking through the experience with a skilled person may stave off PTSD, according to a midwife who has made a special study of the issue, published in *Midwives* (October 1997) – a process discussed further on page 16.

'Victims of Hormones' – Postnatal Depression as a Biochemical Disorder

Fall in Progesterone Levels

For almost thirty years, it's been suggested that one of the major causes of postnatal depression is a drop in levels of the hormone progesterone.

Progesterone is produced in pregnancy (and also in the latter half of the menstrual cycle in women who aren't pregnant). At delivery, progesterone levels fall very rapidly.

The main advocate of this cause of postnatal depression is Katharina Dalton, a doctor who has treated thousands of women for postnatal depression and puerperal psychosis. Her theories and practice still await, after decades, 'systematic evaluation of its clinical impact' - and that has to be a shortcoming, given that other forms of treatment such as counselling, or antidepressants, are studied carefully for their effectiveness and safety compared with doing nothing. A recent review concluded that there was no evidence that progesterone therapy helped.

There is no good reason put forward in Dalton's work of why such a natural event as a fall in progesterone should have such a devastating effect on mood, behaviour and outlook in a substantial minority – she rather dodges the question and, in *Depression After*

Childbirth (Oxford University Press, 1996), instead invites us to marvel at why so many women don't respond in this way.

However, there are many cases where women are convinced they have been helped by progesterone treatment, or they have avoided a second or third postnatal depression altogether by taking the treatment soon after labour. You can read about the treatment on page 58.

Some women feel their postnatal depression has a definite hormonal element:

> 'I was fine until I stopped breastfeeding when my baby was nine months old and my periods returned. Then everything changed. I feel I am vulnerable to hormonal change – I get bad pre-menstrual tension, and I suffer panic attacks which are always related to my menstrual cycle.'

There is reluctance to ascribe postnatal depression to hormones – and not just among scientists who prefer to be convinced by academic papers and research projects, rather than glowing testimonials from patients.

The 'hormone idea' comes in for an especially hard time from writers, midwives and health professionals taking a social view rather than a biochemical one. Sheila Kitzinger, in her book *The Crying Baby* (Viking, 1989) says to blame hormonal disturbance is 'to miss the point' – which to her is the failure of society to give adequate social support to mothers. Psychologist Katherine Paradice, writing in the *British Journal of Midwifery* (December 1995) says 'women do not want to be seen as victims of their hormones, but want the reality of their lives acknowledged'.

Mind Games? Psychotherapy
and Psychiatry

Another medical approach takes the view that something has happened to 'damage' a postnatally depressed woman psychologically, often years ago in childhood.

Psychotherapy

Psychotherapy, a 'talking' therapy which involves long sessions of one-to-one work between therapist and client, would be expected to explore issues in the client's past, including childhood relationships and events.

There is a risk with this approach of looking for psychological causes of depression, according to at least one writer on motherhood: we end up in a mother-blaming scenario, created by theorists who 'have pointed the finger at the bad mother as if she was the cause of all evils', as psychiatrist Jane Price puts it in *Motherhood: What It Does to Your Mind* (Pandora, 1988).

Another writer says that 'the mother has been a convenient scapegoat throughout the centuries', adding that the last century has additional weapons – 'psychology and psychiatry have elevated mother-hating and mother-baiting to the status of scientific fact'.[22]

It's true that the mothers of sufferers are often raised as a point of discussion in therapy for postnatal depression (and other depressions), but unless we are to say that childhood experience has nothing to do with the way we 'turn out' in adulthood, and that a happy or sad childhood has no longer-term effects, we can't argue with the relevance of mothers.

Yes, of course it's important to avoid unnecessary 'blame' by acknowledging, as Price suggests that 'most mothers are ... socially powerless to challenge and change life for themselves, let alone their children. They are only allowed to make changes within the guidelines of what the culture accepts. That culture is laid down ... by men who have avoided the adult reality of parenting young children.'

But given that mothers are often the parent who is closer to the child, it would be astonishing if the mother-daughter relationship didn't have long-lasting effects on the daughter's own experience of motherhood, and indeed, postnatal depression. This relationship can be examined and understood in individual therapy without demonizing mothers in general, surely, or indeed, ignoring any experience of cruel, ignorant, misguided or 'bad' parenting (which may, anyway, have its origins in the grandparents' and great-grandparents' styles of parenting ...). We should recall, though, that any discussion of childhood can't just focus on mothers – fathers have a place as well.

Take this situation, published in *New Generation* in June 1996, which seems to show a strong 'cause and effect':

'Rachel's parents separated when she was one. She never saw her father again. The family went to live with grandparents and she remembers little of her childhood save a distant, working mother made bitter and critical by the hand life had dealt her. Forced into the role of provider, her mother did not allow her children to play with others. This insular upbringing gave Rachel no insight into "normal" family dynamics and left her with a desperate need to do everything right to please her mother.

'Rachel's depression began before leaving hospital with her son. As Rachel herself admits, "I just didn't know how to 'mother' but I was desperate to cope ... added to this, my husband comes from a family of strong, capable women and I could never admit to them I was such a failure." Rachel's mother told her to "pull her socks up and get on with it" and insisted "we don't have mental problems in this family.'"

Fiona Shaw's powerful and involving story of her own postnatal breakdown, already quoted in Chapter 1, is a riveting account of how childhood experiences – and relationships with parents, siblings, and in her case, half-siblings – find some sort of echo in the terrors and griefs she experiences after the birth of her second child.

Shaw can't see exactly how her breakdown is caused by her childhood history, but she knows in some way the links are there. During her recovery, she says she realized:

'I'd made forays into the alarming territory of my own past, finding there the shapes of things to come. I still couldn't explain what happened but at least I saw that it had happened because I was me, living my life.'

Talking to other women about their own experience, she says she comes to see that postnatal depression was 'not some strange interloper of an illness, arriving in the middle of their life from nowhere. Their depression was the expression of something unbearable in the midst of it all, letting rip ... the black flower of postnatal depression has its roots thrust deep into the soil of each person's life.'

Psychotherapy, which involved hours and hours of talk and discussion, the support of family and friends, her own insights and the passage of time eventually helped Shaw back to a kind of contentment, though her experience changed her profoundly.

Daughters All

We don't become parents ourselves without being influenced, at many levels, by our own experiences as a daughter. The very experience of being a mother may stir up quite strong feelings, as we determine, consciously or unconsciously, to do the very opposite to what our mothers (and fathers) did, or the very same, or else we decide in some way to compete with our own parents.

Psychoanalyst Joan Raphael-Leff, in *Pregnancy: the Inside Story* (Sheldon Press, 1993), details the swirling emotional forces that swoop through the generations, shaping our own parenting in ways we don't always understand.

Raphael-Leff points out that, just sometimes, we get a glimpse of these 'ghosts in the nursery'. I bet many of us know just what she means. When my mother told me that she 'trained' us to sleep through the night when we were only a few weeks old by shutting the door on us, and going to a part of the house where she couldn't hear us cry, I felt (and still feel!) a sharp, pitying pang for my poor little baby-self, left to scream without anyone even hearing me. I also knew I would never, could never, do that to my own babies – and I understood why I felt so very strongly about not doing it, too.

Some parents – mothers and fathers – find that unresolved griefs and resentments complicate their responses to their new babies. But therapist Dilys Daws, writing in *New Generation* in September 1997, says her clinical experience shows that people who can remember a difficult childhood are more strongly placed to get over it and make a fresh start with the baby, than those for whom the past remains a blank.

Psychiatry

Psychiatry – the medical study and treatment of mental illness – sometimes takes a rather different approach to postnatal depression. In general, mainstream psychiatry does not have a happy history, especially when it comes to dealing with women.

Writer Elaine Showalter in *The Female Malady* (Virago, 1987) has shown some of the sometimes cruel, often woefully ignorant, treatment of mentally ill (or sometimes just supposedly mentally ill) women in the last 150 years. Middle- and upper-class ladies with any form of emotional disturbance, including the ones suffering from what we would now call postnatal depression, were, for example, at the end of the last century given a 'rest cure' to render them docile, compliant and often very bored. Working-class women would be committed to workhouses or asylums.

Psychoanalysis, which gained ground in the first half of this century, has often been, in its most 'masculine' guise, on a search for a psychiatric, psychological or emotional flaw in women suffering postnatal depression.

Sheila Kitzinger in the book cited above on page 34 quotes from 'experts' who are certain that some women fail to accept their female role (whatever that might be and whoever might define it) and rebel against it psychically. Or they have a pathologically disrupted ego that prevents them from undertaking household chores. The literature also includes some 'gems' such as arguments that postnatal depression was a rejection of 'true' femininity and proof that the sufferer had abnormal unfeminine inclinations, which comprised, among other things, suppressed lesbianism.

Much of this value-laden stuff was written in the 1960s and 70s, and it all sounds very patriarchal and even laughable to our ears. We'll draw a veil over the fact that the 1960s and 70s were when many of today's psychiatrists and medical people were training, hoping that they've done their best to keep up-to-date with changes in the culture. In fairness, too, let's remind ourselves that our own end-of-century cultural prejudices may be looked at askance in a generation's time – we could turn out to be the millennium kettles berating the 1960s pots...

Fiona Shaw details the experience of the psychiatry she encountered. She also recounts her response to the medical textbooks she devoured in an attempt to understand not just the 'why' of her breakdown, but the 'why' of her apparently useless, distressing psychiatric treatment. She feels conventional psychiatry has little to offer the sufferer as an individual in need of help, and even less to offer anyone who actually wants to understand postnatal depression, their own or anyone else's:

> 'Psychiatry tries to make everybody fit into a medical generality. Once a person's behaviour has been given the appropriate technical term they can be forgotten about as someone with a particular life and treated as a condition instead. This is understandable ... but it still leaves the patient in the lurch.'

Of course, this criticism can also be applied to any purely pathological approach – that is, an approach that says that everything that's not 'right' in the body or mind is due to an illness. Good medicine today takes a holistic view, seeing patients as social creatures, and far more than just a collection of symptoms to be labelled. Mainstream psychiatric texts today acknowledge the social and emotional aspects of postnatal depression and how psychotherapy, counselling and social support may be appropriate for some.

'Am I Really Ill?' Postnatal Depression as 'Normal' Unhappiness

'We've just moved house, I have a thyroid cyst diagnosed, I have a toddler and a new baby and I miss my mother, though we talk on the phone a lot. I feel dreadful. Every day is a struggle and a challenge. I have to make a huge effort to get up and get going in the mornings. It's getting dark in the evenings, and I know winter's on the way – and that makes me feel awful, as I hate the winter. I went to the doctor this morning and he gave me some antidepressants, but I don't know if I am going to take them. I'm in two minds, frankly. I mean, am I really ill, or is this just a normal response to my problems?'

Even talking about postnatal 'depression' is controversial today, because it appears to make a clear statement about the range of emotions and behaviours experienced by new mothers. The word 'depression' implies that these emotions and behaviours are an illness, that there's 'something wrong' with the mother, just as if she had a broken leg or an upset stomach.

These days, some researchers and commentators avoid the use of the term. They talk about 'emotional well-being' or 'unhappiness after childbirth' or 'maternal distress'. The medicalization of these feelings, by naming them postnatal depression, is, of course, both a continuation of the medical model of pregnancy and childbirth, and part of the tendency to diagnose any unhappiness as a mental disorder, when it's a natural human reaction to a miserable period of one's life. This very medicalization is, says one commentator, 'one of the greatest disasters of the 20th century.'[23]

Many of us would agree with Littlewood and McHugh's statement, based on the available research, that 'some degree of maternal distress is almost universally present amongst women who have recently given birth.'[24] True enough. Any of us who have had children could take a pen and go through the list of symptoms on page 7 (Chapter 1) and tick off several items – whether or not we have been diagnosed as depressed, or even felt that's what we had. Which new mother hasn't felt tired, confused, anxious, weepy or irritable?

A Scale of Negativity

It may well be that there's a scale of negativity.

New mothers who are mainly (but of course not always) happy and fulfilled, energetic and stable, unworried and not sleepless, are sitting smiling at the bottom of the scale. In the middle, are mothers who experience tiredness, irritability, tearfulness, anxiety, etc. some of the time. And as we get to the top end, we find the mothers who would be diagnosed as having postnatal depression.

The idea of a scale is supported, I would say, in studies of mothers' emotional well-being (EWB). Jean A. Ball's survey in her book *Reactions to Motherhood* (Cambridge University Press, 1987) scored mothers at six weeks after the birth on various important factors such as anxiety, self-confidence, support, satisfaction and coping ability.

She found a range of scores, which she divided into low, moderate and high EWB. On further questioning, mothers with low EWB had symptoms which corresponded very closely with the symptoms of postnatal depression as defined by a classic profile.[25]

I find the image of a scale, or a spectrum, more realistic than one alternative which is to divide women's postnatal depression up into two, namely 'major' and 'minor'. Two authors and clinicians – Peter Nolan and Geoff Alcock, both working in Birmingham – do this in a recent paper in *The Practising Midwife* (January 1998). This is certainly better than assuming everyone's experience is of equal intensity, but still, I feel, hides the fact that only a few women could with confidence be slotted in to either of the two categories.

'Depression' Does Women No Favours

As we've seen, postnatal depression may not be a totally separate clinical entity, so using the label may not be very accurate. The other possible fault with the label, say some experts, is that using it does women a disservice.

'Naming the unhappiness or misery experienced by many women as depression may confine explanations of its [cause or causes] to the biomedical or psychological, while ignoring the context of parenting ... at the individual level, distress may be seen as the personal responsibility of the woman involved ... at the community level [it] avoids the need to look for explanations of women's distress or rethink the social organisation and structures supporting parenting.'[26]

In other words, naming unhappiness as depression risks 'blaming the victim'.

One parent support worker, Anne Jenkins of NEWPIN argues that the term postnatal depression is a 'dangerous catch-all'. In an interview in *Health Visitor* (May 1990) she says some women may become even more depressed if they're given a diagnosis of it, 'because most women believe depression is a form of insanity and therefore [that] they've been labelled insane'.

A large study found that among women who had scored as depressed on the Edinburgh Postnatal Depression Scale (see page 54), and who perceived themselves as depressed, a third did not want to call their experience postnatal depression.[27]

In another survey of 78 women identified as suffering from postnatal depression, while 90 per cent recognized there was something wrong, only a third believed they were suffering from postnatal depression.[28]

There's clearly a reluctance among women to label themselves as being postnatally depressed, but I think the idea that postnatal depression is 'dangerous' as women tend to equate it with 'insanity' probably overstates the case.

In the last generation, depression has become enough of an everyday term for people not to have to shy away in fear. A generation ago, I can recall female friends and relatives were said to be 'bad with their nerves'. I haven't heard the expression used by anyone under about 70 for at least a decade. Today we use terms like 'anxiety state' or 'depression' or 'panic attacks' and have at least a rough idea that they are not the equivalents of 'insanity'.

I also don't see evidence that using the term postnatal depression encourages health professionals to blame mothers, or to avoid looking at parenting circumstances or lack of support.

The medical and nursing journals are full of articles about the social and emotional context of being a parent. Health visitors in particular are at the forefront of community-based initiatives to offer social support to new mothers. Depression of all types is widely accepted as having a social element (for example, as a result of stress after major life events).

However, women who don't want to be labelled as having postnatal depression may be resisting the idea that their feelings are solely as a result of having had a baby. They may be recognizing that there's a lot more 'wrong' in their lives than that ... and they're very often right.

No Wonder We're Depressed!

Some commentators see postnatal depression as a perfectly understandable response to the pressures, and lack of support, inherent in being a mother today.

It's a response to the loss of their old life, and the strain of having to adapt to so many changes, according to Katharine Paradice.

It could be a natural reaction, a trick to conserve emotional energy: 'the depression may actually be a normal part of the experience of motherhood, even an adaptive process, allowing the woman to grieve for her lost self, and to make the transition to motherhood.'[29]

Women get postnatally depressed, say others, as a result of feeling pressure to 'cope' and to act as if everything was wonderful all the time. Motherhood is, after all, 'skilled, demanding and exhausting work,' as Professor Brockington of Birmingham University says in the introduction to *Motherhood and Mental Health* (Oxford University Press, 1998).

Noreen Sweeney, a colleague of Anne Jenkins at NEWPIN and interviewed at the same time, says 'I think there's a great fear of being seen as not coping. It should be okay for people to say "I feel awful". If there's more leeway to do that, perhaps people who get depressed will not get into a really bad state.'

This is sometimes an essentially feminist viewpoint: it holds that the reality of pregnancy, childbirth and early motherhood reflects a woman's position in society, and her status within her family and marital relationships.[30]

In addition, the label of postnatal depression may be a convenient way for society (and men) to put these moaning, troublesome women who refuse to be happy in their new role well and truly in their place again.

Myths of Motherhood

It's easy to observe a contradiction in today's culture: motherhood is on the one hand praised for its importance, and held to be a wonderful, rewarding 'job', and yet on the other, it also goes hand-in-hand with isolation, lack of cash, and a loss of your feeling of identity.

The myth of the permanently fulfilled, satisfied mother with her gorgeous smiling infant refuses to fade. It's odd. Antenatal teachers and indeed other mothers can talk about broken nights, screaming days and still being in your dressing gown at dinner time. But new mothers are still taken aback when it happens to them.

As an author and journalist writing on baby care and family life, I have been taken to task by women who say writers like me 'idealise' motherhood, and we tell them that babies feed every four hours and then sleep all night. I have never written anything of the sort – and nor have I read anything that suggests it in publications from recent years (and I have read a lot of baby care stuff). Baby care books today are at pains to say how hard the job of mothering can be, and how babies are unpredictable and demanding, on the whole.

Somehow or other, pregnant women don't hear the bad news, or think it doesn't apply to them; there are other images that are more powerful, and more persistent. As Noreen Sweeney says, 'I know people try to explain at antenatal classes what it might be like to have a baby, but we're still in a society that has posters with very nice-looking mums and very pretty babies – all terribly normal. I'd actually class posters like that as abnormal because in the main, motherhood isn't like that. Maybe you're better seeing a poster with a big dollop of puke on the shoulder – because that's the reality.'

I'd like to see postnatal depression feature more often in soaps and popular drama. TV stories certainly get the nation talking about 'issues'. Kathy in *EastEnders* was not only a mum in her 40s, but she had some form of postnatal depression when baby Ben was born in 1996. But that's unusual – probably because the reality of most postnatal depression is not dramatic. It progresses slowly and sluggishly. It's not a turn-on for the viewer, and it's uninspiring for the scriptwriter. When TV deals with mental health matters, it tends to go for the all-singing, all-dancing breakdown with knobs on!

Questions and Answers

Q. DOES POSTNATAL DEPRESSION HAPPEN MORE THAN ONCE TO
   THE SAME PERSON?

A. Yes. Previous postnatal depression is a risk factor, but the great
   majority of women who have it once don't have it again.
       Puerperal psychosis is a different matter. Perhaps 20 to 25 per
   cent of women develop it again after subsequent births.[31]

Q. ARE THERE MEDICAL CAUSES FOR POSTNATAL DEPRESSION
   APART FROM THE HORMONAL ONES?

A. Yes. Just occasionally, some physical conditions can cause symptoms of exhaustion and depression in new mothers. These might
   include:
❑ anaemia
❑ dietary deficiencies – potassium, zinc, and vitamin B6 are among
   possible substances the mother may need supplementing with,
   according to Maggie Comport's book on postnatal depression,
   Towards Happy Motherhood (Corgi, 1987).

Ask your doctor or another health professional for their views on a
possible medical or dietary cause of your depression, and whether
tests might be appropriate.

References for Chapter Two

1 K. Paradice. Postnatal depression: a normal response to motherhood? *British Journal of Midwifery*, December 1995.

2 A. Taylor, D. Adams, V. Glover. Postnatal depression: identification, risk factors and effects. *British Journal of Midwifery*, June 1994 .

3 V. Glover *et al*. Mild hypomania, the highs can be a feature of the first postpartum week: association with later depression. *British Journal of Psychiatry*, Vol. 164, No. 4, 1994.

4 A. Stein, P.J. Cooper, E.A. Campbell. Social adversity and perinatal complications: their relationship to postnatal depression. *British Medical Journal*, Vol. 171, 1073–4, 1989.

5 R. Kumar, K.M. Robson. A prospective study of emotional disorders in childbearing women. *British Journal of Psychiatry*, Vol. 144, No. 1, 1984.

6 S.L. Wheatley. Antenatal sources of social support as predictors of early postnatal depression. Unpublished paper from University of Leicester, Section of Social and Epidemiological Psychiatry, 1997.

7 *ibid*.

8 E.S. Paykel *et al*. Life events and social support in puerperal depression *British Journal of Psychiatry*, Vol. 136, 339–46, 1980.

9 N. Posner *et al*. Screening for postpartum depression: an antepartum questionnaire. *Journal of Reproductive Medicine*, April 1997.

10 Kumar and Robson *op.cit*.

11 L. Murray, W. Cartwright. The role of obstetric factors in postpartum depression. *Journal of Reproductive Medicine and Infant Psychology*, Oct/Dec 1993.

12 P.M. Boyce, A.L. Todd. Increased risk of postnatal depression after emergency caesarean section. *Medical Journal of Australia*, 3 August 1992.

13 J.M. Green. Who is unhappy after childbirth? Antenatal and intrapartum correlates from a prospective study. *Journal of Reproductive Medicine and Infant Psychology*, July–September 1990.

14 R. Small *et al*. Depression after childbirth - does social context matter? *Medical Journal of Australia*, 17 October 1994.

15 A. Stein *et al*. *op.cit*.

16 G. Byrne, B. Raphael. Postpartum depression. *Journal of Paediatrics, Obstetrics and Gynaecology*, May–June 1994.

17 R. Small *et al*. Missing voices: what women say and do about depression after childbirth. *Journal of Reproductive and Infant Psychology*, Vol. 12, 89–103, 1994.

18 C.A. Niven. *Psychological Care for Families Before, During and After Birth*, Butterworth Heinemann, 1992.

19 Both cases cited in I. Brockington. *Motherhood and Maternal Health*, Oxford, 1998.

20 Adapted from K.A. Kendall-Thackett, G. Kaufman-Kanter. *Postpartum Depression: a Comprehensive Approach for Nurses*, Sage, 1993.

21 M.J. Scott, S.G. Stradling. *Counselling for Post-traumatic Stress Disorder*, Sage, 1992.

22 J.M. Ussher. *Women's Madness: Misogyny or Mental Illness*, Harvester/Wheatsheaf, 1991.

23 A. Oakley. Beyond the yellow wallpaper or taking women seriously. In A. Oakley (ed) *Telling the Truth about Jerusalem*, Oxford, 1986.

24 J. Littlewood, N. McHugh *op.cit*.

25 B. Pitt. Atypical depression following childbirth. *British Journal of Psychiatry*, Vol. 114, 1325–351, 1968.

26 L.M. Barclay, B. Lloyd. The misery of motherhood: alternative approaches to maternal distress. *Midwifery*, Vol. 12, 136–9, 1996.

27 R. Small *op.cit*.

28 A. Whitton, R. Warner, L Appleby. The pathway to care in post-natal depression: women's attitudes depression and treatment. *British Journal of General Practice*, July 1996.

29 J. Ussher. Reproductive rhetoric and the blaming of the body. In P. Nicholson, J. Ussher (eds). *The psychology of Women's Health and Health Care*, Macmillan, 1992.

30 For example, C. Jebali. A feminist perspective on postnatal depression. *Health Visitor*, February 1993.

31 Action on Puerperal Psychosis Newsletter, April 2002.

3

Getting Help with Postnatal Depression

'It's difficult to ask for help – because that means admitting failure ...'

Help, of several different kinds, should be available for anyone suffering from postnatal depression in the UK.

But there's plenty of evidence to show that when women recognize depression or severe unhappiness at this time, they may be reluctant to seek help.

In one study, only two out of five women identified as depressed at eight to nine months postpartum had sought any professional advice about it.[1] In another, 80 per cent of women identified as depressed at six to eight weeks had not spoken about their feelings to any professional.[2]

It can be hard to ask for help – and some women don't realize something can be done. Some women feel they don't deserve to seek help, or feel guilty and ashamed at not being 'Ms Happy Mummy'. Anything that happens is their fault, because they are worthless and hopeless.

'I'd been depressed after my first child, and with the third I had an inkling it was happening again. By six weeks I was certain. But I couldn't bear the idea of facing up to it. My husband hadn't wanted a third child, and I couldn't tell him I was depressed again. It was 14 months before I went to my doctor.'

'I tried to convince everyone I was fine. I knew I was okay if I stayed at home. I'd put the answering machine on so if anyone phoned they'd think I'd gone out, and wouldn't realize I was in a bad way. I put a curtain up so no one could see through the glass of the front door if they came to call, and guess I was in.'

'I found it difficult to admit I needed help – not necessarily medical help – just an outlet, a valve to open when the pressure rose.'

Clare Delpech, from the Association of Postnatal Illness, told the *Guardian* in February 1997, 'there's a great hesitation to say to [the health visitor] "I can't cope". They have a real fear the health visitor might contact the social services and the baby might be taken away.'

When I was a newish mother, caring for a baby and a toddler, I had a friend with two children the same age, a woman I saw three or four times a week for coffee or to share childcare or to go shopping. Before I knew her, she'd had postnatal depression, quite badly, with her first child.

When her second baby was about six months old, I learned that for the past five months, she was regularly breaking down in tears in the late afternoon, and calling her husband at work, begging him to come home early. Some mornings, she couldn't cope at all, and made her husband stay at home. But to me, and our circle of friends, she seemed fine. The massive effort she made to look and act normal, she told me later, sprang from a feeling of guilt and shame that again, she seemed to be the only mother finding life impossible.

Where Help May Come From

The Health Service

Every new mother can call on the services of a midwife, and later, of a health visitor, and she and her baby are normally registered with a family doctor as well. Either of these three can be the first health professional you approach if you feel you want to talk about your feelings and concerns.

Through the health service, you can be referred to a psychiatrist, clinical psychologist or community psychiatric nurse (CPN) if it's thought appropriate. The CPN normally visits at home, though you would probably see the psychiatrist or psychologist at a hospital out-patients' clinic.

In fact, most mothers with postnatal depression are not referred to the psychiatric services, though local protocols differ. In some places, all 'front line' health professionals (the midwives, GPs and health visitors) are trained in spotting postnatal depression, and specialist referral is always made for women who show severe symptoms.

More often, your health visitor and/or family doctor is the source of health service help. Typically, you see your doctor to discuss any medication, and your health visitor may see you at home or in the clinic.

The Importance of Your Health Visitor

Increasingly, health visitors are 'leading players' in the help offered to a woman with postnatal depression. They can refer for medical help, but more importantly, they can get to know a mother, and what constitutes her circumstances, the way she is with her baby and the people close to her. They can support her themselves with extra visits, and they should know what sort of support there is in the mother's area by way of National Childbirth Trust groups, mother and baby groups, or special postnatal depression groups.

In December 1991, *Health Visitor* reported on the lack of help for postnatal depression from health professionals and the poor level of training among health visitors: 'The area represents a professional minefield. There are no clear guidelines for joint effort ... and no clear identification of the skills and competence required to deal with depressed mothers with young children.'

Already, though, the situation is improved; the training and knowledge among health professionals is now a lot better than it was. The health visitors' professional body, the Community Practitioners' and Health Visitors' Association (CPHVA), has initiated training schemes and conferences, often held in conjunction with other lay and professional groups. Their professional journal has been an important publisher of research on postnatal depression, and regularly includes accounts of support initiatives started or encouraged by health visitors. You can read about some of them below.

Health visitors are, after all, in a good position to detect postnatal depression, as they see mothers at home and in the baby clinic. In some areas, health visitors are trained to use the Edinburgh Postnatal Depression Scale (EPDS) as a way of helping them diagnose women who may be postnatally depressed.

The EPDS is a brief questionnaire, normally used at 6–8 weeks after the birth, and/or 6–8 months after the birth. It asks a mother what her mood and feelings have been in the last week. It's simple to use and it doesn't pry into personal experiences a mother may not want to share. Just as importantly, in the academic jargon it's been well validated – that is, used with proven effectiveness, in many places. High scorers are far more likely to be depressed than low scorers, and the health visitor can, as it were, take things from there.

Routine use of the EPDS is widely recommended[3] as long as health visitors are trained in its use, and able to offer the appropriate help to mothers whose scores are high. Proper use of the scale is essential... as one health visitor-researcher explains, warning about limitations: 'The scale is only as good as the person interpreting it. Where there is no (or inadequate) training, individual health visitors will use it as best they can, but this may not be good enough.'[4]

Using the questionnaire is undoubtedly an effective way of revealing the possibility of postnatal depression; it may also give a woman 'permission' to really say how she's feeling:

> 'When I heard the health visitor was going to come round and test me with the scale, I thought "thank goodness for that. Now I can let it all out." I got a high score – and when she told me this, I just burst into tears.'

What Can Health Professionals Do?

Mothers can get counselling from health professionals – a form of talking therapy which gives an opportunity to talk honestly about feelings and circumstances, without being judged or criticized. When appropriate, the counsellor, whoever it is (within the health service, probably a CPN or health visitor) may also help the mother explore different ways of coping, and suggest some practical strategies. There is some use of cognitive behaviour therapy among both CPNs and health visitors.

A health visitor or CPN may visit the mother at regular intervals for a time, and suggest a support group or introduce her to one (see pages 131-133 – though very depressed mothers may not feel able to join a group for a while). In some areas these may be called 'listening visits'. They may number half a dozen or so. When therapeutic visits have been evaluated, they have been found to be effective in alleviating mothers' depression, and appear to have long-term benefits in improving the relationship between the mothers involved and their babies.[5]

Medication

Medication for postnatal depression covers a range of options. Here's an overview of the most commonly prescribed types:

❑ hormones – progesterone or oestrogen
❑ antidepressant drugs, of which there are many. Ones commonly prescribed for postnatal depression include lofepramine (brand name Gamanil), imipramine (Tofranil), clomipramine (Anafranil). Newer forms of antidepressant drugs are known as serotonin (5HT) reuptake inhibitors; one commonly used for postnatal depression is fluoxetine, better known under its brand-name of Prozac. Others used include sertraline (Zoloft), fluvoxamine (Faverin), paroxetine (Paxil).

Progesterone Therapy

Progesterone therapy (see page 33) is given via pessaries (inserted into the anus or the vagina) or injections. Although progesterone therapy is sometimes prescribed by doctors, there has been very little evaluation of its impact.

Oestrogen Therapy

Oestrogen therapy, given via skin patches, looked hopeful at one time, but it is rarely given now. More studies are needed 'to establish the minimum effective dose and the shortest necessary duration of treatment'.[6] It's also not known if oestrogen would help with less severely depressed women.

Antidepressants

Antidepressant drugs, normally given in tablet form, have been used for some time, and have been shown to help in cases of non-postnatal depression and postnatal depression. If you and your doctor decide on this option, more than one type may need to be tried out before you find the one that works best for you. Many types may need two to six weeks to have a full effect, so you can't be sure of the full effect until you have taken them for at least this length of time.

You should expect some side-effects with all of them. Side-effects may include:

- dry mouth
- nausea
- constipation
- diarrhoea
- drowsiness.

Prozac has become more widely prescribed in recent years, and so far, doctors reckon side-effects seem to be less of a problem – though it's still regarded with caution by some experts. Other drugs are probably preferable when a mother is breastfeeding.

An interesting study compared the effects of Prozac with the effects of counselling. It found that they were both equally effective, and that there was no advantage to receiving both counselling and Prozac.[7]

This could be a very important finding. It means women who don't wish to use medication can be reassured that counselling is just as likely to work.

One issue that then arises is the availability of counselling, and its cost, versus the cost of drugs. Medication may be the cheaper, and easier, way of treating postnatal depression. Ideally, though, given that counselling works, women should be free to choose it.

Other Medications

Other medication includes tranquillizers and sedatives such as diazepam (Valium), chlordiazepoxide (Librium); more powerful anti-depressants known as monoamine oxidase inhibitors (MAOIs), such as phenelzine (Nardil); sleeping tablets like temazepam (Mogadon).

These ones are less commonly prescribed for postnatal depression than antidepressants, because of their side-effects, and because their sedative effect may make it difficult to stay 'together' enough to undertake the demanding task of looking after a baby.

Thyroid hormones can be prescribed for women whose symptoms of depression are associated with thyroid disturbance (about 1 per cent, according to one paper)[8]. This work is still fairly new, and thyroid disturbance, which affects about 5 per cent of women after childbirth, is not easy to diagnose, but some researchers suggest it is worth investigating as a cause, and treatment prescribed – perhaps with antidepressants.

St John's Wort

In the past few years, the herb St John's Wort has been suggested as a treatment for mild-to-moderate depression and some of the research on it is encouraging. But its use in the treatment of postnatal depression hasn't been studied yet, and there is no information according to Thomas Hale's *Medications and Mother's Milk* (Pharmasoft, 2000) on its transfer to breastmilk. So although Hale suggests that it probably doesn't penetrate the milk well, he says other, better suited products should be used instead. There's certainly no evidence that St John's Wort is better for breastfeeding mothers just because it is herbal.

For How Long?

Antidepressants or any other medication should never be the only help you get with postnatal depression, though in many situations they do have a role to play. You should note that many women need to take them for a long time – often several months. If you use antidepressants, you should withdraw from them gradually when the time comes to stop using them.

Chemical dependence on antidepressants is not normally a problem. Antidepressants are not the same as tranquillizers, where there's a known risk of addiction and where withdrawal, after long-term use, even gradual, can bring serious problems of its own.

Getting Together – Support Groups and Postnatal Depression

There are hundreds of postnatal support groups in the UK – the exact number would be hard to be precise about. Some are locally grown initiatives which come and then go after the 'leading lights' move on; some are run by health visitors or other professionals, which are only ever temporary as they are part of a time-limited research project, or linked to hospital outpatients' groups.

The social support and friendship offered by groups is very important. Medication, counselling and non-critical listening sessions can only go so far – they don't relieve the loneliness and isolation women experience.

Many lay (non-health professional) groups are affiliated to larger organizations like NCT, MAMA (Meet-a-Mum Association), the Association for Postnatal Illness and Homestart. You can find out addresses and telephone numbers of groups on pages 131–133, plus details of helplines. Health visitors and midwives should know of local groups in your area. Some groups may focus on baby massage, which can help mothers whose depression makes them feel 'distant' from their babies, as it's usually enjoyable for both mother and baby, and it's a skill a mother can learn which is soothing and simple.

Carole Jeffrey, who has herself suffered from postnatal depression, helps to run a MAMA-affiliated group in Trafford, Manchester. 'Over the last five years or so, we reckon we have helped about 300 mothers,' she says. 'We offer one-to-one support on the telephone and there's a weekly group support meeting on a Friday.' The group meetings are not miserable occasions. 'There's a great deal of laughter. Being a group of women who feel the same as you can be very liberating.'

Group support offers five components that help, says Pat Eastwood, who wrote about her experiences as a health visitor starting up a group in Bexley, in *Health Visitor* (April 1995):

- ❑ it offers confidentiality – women can discuss their depression in a safe, non-judgemental setting
- ❑ there is counselling, through talking to other mothers with postnatal depression
- ❑ it helps women focus on their own needs, thoughts and feelings.

- they can share and discover that their feelings are similar to other mothers'
- they can find support by being cared for, and by being caring towards, others in the group.

When mothers were asked by Eastwood and colleagues what benefits they'd received from their course of meetings, they said they felt safe in the group, and were encouraged to be honest and not made to feel guilty. Evaluation showed that members' self-esteem had increased, and they scored consistently lower on a scale designed to rate depressive symptoms (Beck Depression Inventory).

Small groups (no more than 10) seem to work better, as women can get to know each other well. Severely depressed women may not feel able to attend – getting out of bed and getting themselves and the baby dressed is enough of a mountain to climb for them. Being at a certain place at a set time and interacting with people they have never met before may be too much. The role of groups may be to support women who are less severely disabled by their depression. Initial one-to-one support may be needed before women feel they can join a group.

Not all groups help everybody that goes to them. Some women may feel worse, listening to the experiences of women who may have suffered badly, especially if the group has members who are very severely depressed. Groups that are poorly organized, poorly focused, may have at best an ephemeral effect.

Fiona Shaw went along to the monthly support group run by the hospital she had been treated in during the worst part of her experience.

Her book, *Out of Me*, explains how at first she had no desire to go, but then she felt 'a morbid pull' to attend. 'Possessed by an anxiety' she walks down the long corridor to the ward. She attends for several months before giving up on it.

'No one felt free of their illness and all were bewildered, with no way of describing or understanding what had happened ... none of the nurses who organized the group was willing to offer any opinions about the causes, treatment or recovery from postnatal depression. They seemed unsure of the point of the group, expecting the women to know what it was they were coming for. Since all the women, myself included, were in varying states of confusion, embarrassment and anxiety about what had happened, no one was in a position to do this.'

A run-of-the-mill mother and baby or toddler group, not especially targeted at mothers with postnatal depression, may not be ideal, either. If you're feeling terrible, and inadequate, and guilty, what does the sight of a roomful of happy, chattering mums do to you? It might not cheer you up...

'When you go to NCT coffee groups, everyone is bright and cheerful and capable. I found I didn't say very much. They all seemed to be so much better at being a mum.'

Anna McGrail quotes a mother who felt worse after attending a group, in *Becoming a Family* (NCT Publishing 1996):

'...the girl who lives in the basement flat said come along to one of these NCT things, and I thought, "oh I don't want to do that, it sounds like everyone sitting around eating butterfly cakes." But she persuaded me and I went with her...and it was horrendous. Everyone was sitting round eating these flapjacks. I felt like a fish out of water and when I came home I felt even worse because I thought I'd never find anyone I could really share my feelings with.'

Now there's nothing wrong with flapjacks (or butterfly cakes, for that matter). But if you see women eating them confidently, and sort of 'sitting around' in a comfortable and relaxed manner, as a depressed mother you see the gap between your world and the world of the flapjack eaters. It makes you feel alone.

Getting There in the First Place

Often, making the effort to attend takes all the energy a woman has.

> 'I knew I needed company of some sort. Twice I went along to the mums and toddlers. Twice I got as far as the front door and went away. The third time I forced myself to go in and sit down, wanting someone to speak to me, but scared if I opened my mouth I'd burst into tears.'

One postnatal supporter remembers her experience with a depressed mother. 'We became NCT junkies – we went to every picnic, every coffee morning, every play session. She was afraid to drive, so we'd go together in my car. Mostly, it helped her, and she'd be all right, and yet other times she'd get somewhere and then decide she couldn't cope. She'd pick up the baby and just walk off.'

Going to a new place with new people is bad enough for non-depressed mothers. I remember a truly awful toddler group I went to – once. Forty mothers sat in a vast church hall, in cliques of three or four. I was newly pregnant, and we had just moved into the area. I knew no one, but I had plucked up courage to ask one of the mothers at my daughter's new playgroup to take me. I sat on my own, watching my toddler son ride a pedal car, for an hour and a half. Not one mother talked to me – not even the mother who had agreed to take me, who made sure she dumped me at the door as soon as she got there. (I've never forgotten her and that small act of unkindness!) All these years later, I remember the despair and overwhelming awkwardness and anger I felt – though I'm pretty sure I looked calm enough. If I'd been depressed, what on earth would that experience have done to me?

That's not to say that groups like NCT's neighbourhood groups – sometimes called postnatal support groups, or 'bumps and babes' or 'drop-ins' – aren't helpful to many mothers, depressed or not. Mothers, including depressed mothers, have told me NCT has been 'a lifeline'. In my own case, I have an abiding memory of the support, friendship and good times I had with NCT when my own children were small. But if you see a mother sitting on her own at a group, she's not being stand-offish or unfriendly. Face it, if she didn't want friends she'd have stayed at home. She may be shy, she may be tired, she may depressed … please talk to her.

Exercise and Postnatal Depression

Health visitor, Anna May, in Dundee founded and ran a postnatal relaxation and exercise class for women in her area suffering from postnatal depression. A creche next door to the exercise room cared for the babies. Asked to evaluate the course, the women were very positive, and reported improved well-being.

Relaxation has an excellent pedigree as a help to general depression, and women in May's group rated it highly. May hypothesized that exercise would increase self-esteem by helping the women regain their shape, and that exercising to lively music would help lift their mood. The women liked the exercise, and some said they did it at home, too.

However, the aspect of the class they found most beneficial was the opportunity for discussion, built in to each session during the coffee breaks. May's own assessment says the course showed the 'importance of peer group social contact in providing the opportunity for women to have baby-free time to themselves.'

One-to-one Support

The National Childbirth Trust also has postnatal supporters, volunteer mothers who offer friendship and a listening ear to any new mother. Mothers who have recovered from postnatal depression are on the 'experiences register', and they can make themselves available, usually as a telephone contact, to a postnatally-depressed mother who wants to share her experience.

NCT's postnatal support guidelines recognize the importance of confidentiality, and time to listen. The supporter is there to support, 'not to advise, diagnose, counsel or judge'.

A supporter says how her relationship with a depressed mother began:

'The mother lived in my street, and she had a son who was born soon after I had my third baby. I first saw her when she was pregnant, and looking back, I think she was already quite depressed. Then I saw her when the baby was 10 days old – and I noticed he was always in his cot whenever I called. She didn't seem to like handling him – when she had to pick him up, she'd hold him away from her – not cuddled in to her, ever.

'She and I got on well, and she was able to feel okay about talking to me. She told me she hated the constant demands the baby made on her, and she never felt any pleasure in the baby's company. I was able to support her in her decision to see the doctor after about four weeks, and fortunately the doctor was really good – she gave her counselling and anti-depressants which did seem to help.

'This mother was so needy – anything that required any sort of organisation was hard for her. She needed to talk, and we spoke often on the phone as well as face to face. I can see how supporters sometimes get quite overwhelmed by the whole thing, and I certainly needed the support of my branch, and other friends, too.

'We became close friends, and as she got better I could see that under the depression she was a really lively person. When she was depressed, no one could see the whole person.'

Other organizations, like MAMA or the Association for Postnatal Illness, also offer one-to-one support, face-to-face or on the telephone. For contacts, see pages 131–133.

Mothers Say What Helped Them

A mother writing in the Association for Postnatal Illness newsletter in April 1997 outlined the list of things that helped her recover:

'The Community Psychiatric Nurse visited me at home, and we talked about coping strategies. I had a good network of support from family, friends, GP, health visitor and church. I felt some responsibility for my recovery and more in control because I listened to a relaxation tape at bedtime. I also made myself get dressed each day, no matter how ill I felt. I was advised to try not to "think", just "be", living each moment as it comes. My husband and I paid for some childcare on a temporary basis, which was a difficult decision for me.'

Other Mothers' Stories

'Nowadays I have learned there is a time when it's okay to be selfish. I have learned at last to make time for myself, and to allow myself that time without feeling guilty.'

'I survived because I had a loving husband and family, and most sympathetic health visitor, who together supported me for many months.'

'I did the work during the day that I could manage to do without tiring myself, and if I couldn't manage to do something which needed doing, I had to learn to leave it until the next day. Gradually I did more and more each day, and although the going was slow and frustrating sometimes, my tiredness was disappearing and with it, the depression.'

'At four months my doctor put me on imipramine. The side-effects were horrible – I had a bad taste in my mouth all the time, and I suffered from nausea. What was worse, I just felt like a zombie. After two weeks, things eased and my mood became a bit lighter, but it didn't get any better from that. When S. was six months, I decided to give up breastfeeding, and that meant I could go onto Prozac. After three weeks, I felt a lot better.'

'The pills I took – lofepramine – helped, as after a fortnight I could feel myself getting gradually better. The heavy, sluggish feeling I had dragged round with for the previous months started to lift.'

Spending time doing things for yourself, away from your baby, can help some mothers. This could be a job, as long as you are not putting even more pressure on yourself or your time. But it can also be a regular few hours off, for a break. A postnatal supporter told me of a mother who left her baby with a childminder for a few mornings a week. 'This was good for the baby as well, as the childminder was a happy, outgoing sort of woman who was happy to carry the baby round for hours, which the mother felt unable to do.'

One mother found things started to get better after her husband insisted they went on holiday. She found her confidence grew. 'The first three days were sheer hell, but by the end of the week I'd discovered it doesn't matter if the baby clothes aren't spotless and that disposable nappies are as good as towelling ones and surely if I'd coped with all the baby paraphernalia away, I could also cope at home.'

Sixty mothers who'd been depressed were asked what advice they would give to other women in a similar situation. These were the most commonly offered responses:

- ❏ find someone to talk to
- ❏ find time for yourself
- ❏ get out among other people
- ❏ seek counselling.[9]

How Long Does it Take to Get Better?

If you have postnatal depression, then it is almost certain you will recover – in time. The worst of the bad feelings can last several weeks or months, and 'overnight' improvement is unlikely. If you are treated with antidepressants, you'll be told it takes two or three weeks for the effects to be felt. If you don't start to feel better after this time, your doctor will probably advise you to return, and your dose, or choice of medication, can be changed.

Counselling and social support — friendship and group support — are likely to give you a short-lived lift at the time you're having them, and the overall, longer-term effects will be gradual and subtle.

Not everyone wants to seek outside help, as we've seen, and in some cases, the 'cure' happens simply by the feelings of depression fading as the mother gains in confidence and emotional strength. But of the women I spoke to who sought treatment, none regretted it and many felt quite definitely that it played an important part in their recovery.

It is not uncommon for women to feel that an entire year after their baby's birth has been dominated by depression, but most women start to feel the worst is over some time before then. 'Feeling better' typically runs a rocky course, with good days and bad days — with the good days gradually outnumbering the bad.

'Eight months on, the depression was coming in waves, rather than being continuously black. Then, at 10 months, I suddenly realized I was enjoying life again. Now, after 18 months, there has been no miraculous cure. I still have very real days and weeks of despair, but I feel that once again I am in tune with myself.'

'After 12 months, I still take Prozac twice a week, and I am learning to say "no" to things I don't want to do, or don't have time for. I have had to learn to delegate. Now my daughter is a toddler, she is so much easier to look after — if she cries, I know it's out of frustration or she's hurt herself or something. Before I was at a loss to deal with her cries, as I just didn't know what to do. She has developed a real personality, and we have a good relationship. Yes, I still have one or two bad days in 10, but maybe everyone has them – life's not totally wonderful for everyone all the time, is it? I can now ring my husband on an especially difficult day, and if he can, he comes home sooner.'

Putting a great deal of pressure on yourself to get better quickly may not help, and may make you feel worse – it's the equivalent of saying 'pull yourself together'. One mother found she was given good advice in the hospital where she'd stayed for a week after a breakdown. 'I was to take one day at a time. I found this helped me to cope better, and I didn't feel overwhelmed by the future as much.'

Here's what one mother wrote for a booklet issued by a support group in Trafford, Manchester. She had suffered from severe postnatal depression, and was admitted to hospital with her baby for treatment, where staff were patient and sympathetic and remembered that mothers 'are part of a family unit which needs to be treated as a whole'. She wrote:

'The question "will I get better?" will arise. Yes, you will! It may take a while, but almost everyone who has suffered from this illness does recover. I was helped a great deal by a support group of sufferers who understood the problems themselves ... There is hope, and you will get there.'

Questions and Answers

Q. CAN I TAKE MEDICATION AND CONTINUE TO BREASTFEED
MY BABY?

A. Yes. I hear from far too many women that they have been told
they can't be treated unless they give up breastfeeding - and as
one mother said to me, 'do I have to? It's the one thing I am getting right.' Some medication is preferable, because it's been
shown to be safe,[10] and Prozac is not the antidepressant of choice
for Dr Thomas Hale, whose textbook *Medications and Mother's
Milk* (Pharmasoft, 2000) looks at evidence that for new mothers
especially, other antidepressants are preferable.

The advice on which drugs to use may change, and you
should in any case always tell your doctor if you are breastfeeding. If you want to continue, then it should be possible to
select a medication to make this possible. Breastfeeding may be
important to both of you emotionally, and of course weaning
from the breast has health implications for both you and your
baby. You may want to discuss your options with a breastfeeding
counsellor first. NCT breastfeeding counsellors have access via
the organization to up-to-date pharmacological information, and
while they cannot give you medical advice, they can let you know
what the current recommendations are for combining breastfeeding with any prescription or over-the-counter drug.

(For more information about postnatal depression and breastfeeding, see page 108.)

References for Chapter Three

1   R. Small *et al*. Missing voices: what women say and do about depression after childbirth. *Journal of Reproductive and Infant Psychology*, Vol. 12, 89–103, 1994.

2   A. Whitton, R. Warner, L. Appleby. The pathway to care in postnatal depression: women's attitudes to postnatal depression and its treatment. *British Journal of General Practice*, July 1996.

3   For example, CRAG Working Group on Maternity Services. Report on detection and early intervention in postnatal depression, Edinburgh 1996.

4   S. Seeley. Strengths and limitations of the Edinburgh Postnatal Depression Scale. CPHVA Conference Proceedings, October 2001.

5   S. Seeley, L. Murray, P.J. Cooper. The outcome for mothers and babies of health visitor intervention. *Health Visitor*, April 1996.

6   A. Gregoire *et al*. Transdermal oestrogen for treatment of severe postnatal depression. *Lancet*, 6 April 1996.

7   L. Appleby *et al*. A controlled study of fluoextine and cognitive-behavioural counselling in the treatment of postnatal depression. *British Medical Journal*, 29 March 1997.

8   B. Harris. A hormonal component in postnatal depression. *British Journal of Psychiatry*, October 1993.

9   R. Small *et al*. Missing voices: what women say and do about depression after childbirth. *Journal of Reproductive and Infant Psychology*, Vol. 12, 89–103, 1994.

10 V. Hendrick *et al*. Use of sertraline, paroxetine and fluvoxamine by nursing women. *British Journal of Psychiatry*, Vol. 179, 163–166, 2001.

4

Postnatal Depression: Your Partner, Your Family

'Looking back, I feel sure he was just as depressed as I was.'

Child psychotherapist Dilys Daws, at a major conference on postnatal depression in 1996, asked an important question. 'Who supports the father? He is also prone to depression ... as much as the mother he has had experiences, good or bad, which will directly affect his baby. It is very easy for an apparently benign conspiracy of females to leave the father out at this point.'

Sad to say, there is plenty of evidence for that 'benign conspiracy'. There is hardly any research work looking at men as new fathers, or men as the partners of depressed new mothers.

This situation should surprise us, given the fact that we know that a close, supportive relationship is an important factor in preventing depression as well as aiding recovery.

More focus on males could have benefits not just for the men, but also for the women and babies in their families. According to a psychiatrist in the field, the lack of knowledge and support does no one any favours. 'In all other areas of medicine, especially psychiatry, we talk about the family as a whole unit, yet fathers are offered no counselling. Health visitors are only interested in them if they're worried the baby's being battered.'[1]

This is not the place to argue that the whole history of medical research in general, and socio-psychological research in particular, is shot through with gender bias. The right questions are sometimes not asked of the right people – so no wonder we get, at best, only half the picture.

Some gaps are, however, being filled. Commentary and research on men and postnatal depression, little as it is, has revealed some important findings:

- ❏ When one partner is depressed, the whole relationship is affected by conflict and tension. Both partners have sadder, more angry, more mistrusting and more detached feelings towards each other. Living with a depressed partner can be a 'considerable burden' for the non-depressed partner, according to Malcolm George, speaking at the conference cited above.
- ❏ The effect on a couple's partnership can be serious. Partners of postnatally-depressed mothers viewed their babies, and their marital relationship, more negatively than the partners of mothers who weren't depressed.[2]
- ❏ Depression leads a sufferer to express hostility, inwardly and outwardly directed. A typically male response to this, according to research, is to withdraw from the conflict, or to express hostility in return. Either way, it can make the depressed mother feel worse, the relationship rocks – and the problems increase.[3]
- ❏ Men can become prone to depression after the first three months.[4]
- ❏ The more fathers become committed and caring, then the more vulnerable they are to the pressures of relationships, to being affected by their partner's depression, and to being prone to depression themselves, says Dilys Daws.

In other words, the new mother is having a rotten time – and so, perhaps, is the new father.

More work needs to be done. For example, we need to see how many men 'catch' postnatal depression from their wives – that is, is their misery a direct result of the tensions of living with a depressed or miserable partner? How many men develop depression independently of their partner's state of mind? And could this, in its turn, be a contributing factor to any subsequent depression in the woman?

One study found 20 per cent of men were depressed six months after becoming a father – the same figures as the researchers found in women at the same time.[5] A Birmingham study found that 10 per cent of fathers were depressed six weeks after the birth, falling to 5 per cent six months later (compared to 27 and 25 per cent of their partners). Men were more likely to be depressed if their partners were, too.

> 'As she got worse, I felt I could cope less and less. I became
> very anxious, I lost a lot of confidence, lost my sex drive ...
> I started drinking a lot. I think it was my way of saying "I've
> got a problem, too". I'd go and have a couple of beers after
> work, just to get Dutch courage to go home and face it all again.'

It could also be that men suffer post-traumatic stress disorder after witnessing a difficult or distressing birth.[6]

The prevailing idea is that being there for the birth of your baby is the world's greatest experience. For some, yes, it's true, but I know I'm not the only woman to have squinted at her husband between her contractions and noticed his green face.

One father was interviewed in *Prima Baby*, Winter 1997/98 issue. He felt that the birth of his baby was gruesome:

'The birth was awful and I wish I hadn't been there. Pauline was in a lot of pain but I felt so helpless as there was nothing I could do to help her. At one point I even asked Pauline for a puff of gas and air myself, but she was clinging on to it for dear life. Then, as the midwife encouraged her to bear down I felt faint and the midwife had to sit me down with a glass of water. Our daughter looked like a gremlin when she first came into the world, not like the healthy pink babies you see on the TV ads.'

A Man's Gotta Do ... What?

Michael's experience on pages 97–99 shows just how confused and distressed a father can feel when his partner is depressed.

Does today's dad help the mother, sympathise with her, or take over some of the baby care? What if that rubs the mother up the wrong way – maybe he takes over too much and she gets to wonder what her role is and if she's any good at it? Does he seek support from her for his own feelings (given that he may be struggling with his own unhappiness and disappointment)? Are his friends any good at listening – probably not, unless it's about blokey topics like sport or work. A man might deny his own feelings and do other things, like staying late at work, or going out to the pub and finding other excuses to be out of the home.

Fathers used to be invisible creatures, expected to bring home the bacon and hang back from any active involvement until the new baby became able to play football or needed pocket money or discipline.

And while I suspect the man who refused to ever change a nappy or push the pram was as much a rarity 40 years ago as the man who was delighted to do everything and anything, active sharing and caring as a delight (or a duty) in the messier bits of baby care is a new idea.

Today, New Dad is a touchy-feely, lovey-dovey square-jawed hunk. He's used to advertise everything from cars to aftershave, and no product aimed at the thinking man is without its media campaign depicting a bare chest and a pair of well-toned biceps cradling a peachy-skinned poppet.

It could be that men, just like women, are overburdened with high expectations, and a matching high level of confusion about what they're really supposed to do. As Dilys Daws says, 'fathers may be equally churned up as mothers by the change in their way of life and status, by the awesome responsibility for a new life, both in physically keeping a vulnerable little body alive, and more long-term provision for an extra member of the family. For men, it might be any of this, but it cannot be blamed on their hormones!'

Steve, for example, felt guilty because he didn't bond with his baby daughter Chloe straight away. 'I was quite distant at first and just saw her as this little screaming thing in the corner. I didn't like her because of the way she changed my wife.' When his second child was born, sibling rivalry turned Chloe into a 'little horror'. Steve felt exhausted, and slept badly. There was no one to confide in. He said, 'I've had a little cry now and again but it's more out of anger'.

Mothers Speak of Their Experiences

Many of the mothers I spoke to acknowledged the effect of depression on their partner, and on their relationship:

'My baby is 12 months old now, and I feel I am recovering. But my poor husband is very low. He is about to start counselling.'

'I sensed my husband was slipping away from me as I got worse – he didn't like my dependency. He had a relationship with someone else – was that caused by my postnatal depression? I don't know. I know it only made me feel more inadequate.'

One mother who had been depressed with children one and three was okay with child number two – but felt her husband was depressed, and on edge. 'He was terrified postnatal depression would recur – I was tired, and I would snap at him, and he'd look at me as if to say "oh God, no ... she's getting that way again". We had no roof on the house and the place was full of workmen, but I coped better than he did. Two years later we had our third child, and I think that was a mistake. He's stretched my husband and me to absolute breaking point.'

Helping Depressed Fathers

Health visitors are in an excellent position to offer help to fathers, and to watch for depression or signs of stress and strain. Taking a direct interest in the father could be an essential part of the health visitor's first and subsequent visits to a new family.

Sadly, there are probably far fewer health visitors than families need – in some areas the health visiting service is under severe threat, and many health visitors say their caseloads are unacceptably full. Once you start looking for postnatal distress, in men or in women, you are bound to find it ... we don't want burnt-out health visitors, or mothers and babies missing out on care because attention's turned to men.

I don't hold out much hope for the other obvious idea, either, I'm afraid: the self-help or support group. Most men run a mile at the notion of sharing their innermost sadness and disappointments with a bunch of others. The few men's discussion groups, or fathers' evenings, that get off the ground – often as a byproduct of an ante-natal class, and facilitated by a father (maybe the antenatal teacher's husband) – seem to be successful as one-offs. They have a tendency to lack staying power. They run out of things to talk about.

I'm like most mothers – I can talk for England with any mother of any age and background about pregnancy, birth, feeding, kids. It's a universal conversational currency for us. Fathers are different. Comedian Billy Connelly satirized the way men talk about childbirth and babies (if they talk about them at all) with a routine about men in a pub comparing gory birth stories without much sensitivity or concern for feelings. Fathers Direct is a sensitive website supporting dads: www.fathersdirect.com

What's Needed

We want some good, qualitative and quantitative research about men and postnatal depression. Let's find out how and why it happens, and test out what would help. Counselling? Antidepressants? Marital or family therapy with partners? Letting time pass so the depressed father gets better by himself (at some cost to his marriage and his partner's happiness, perhaps)? At the moment, we just don't know. And we need to. We need to accept that women and babies usually come in a package deal with fathers and other family members, and that caring for a mother with postnatal depression should not exclude caring for her partner.

Men could be screened for postnatal depression - the Edinburgh Scale (see page 54) has already been used with men and found to be a tool with potential.[7]

I think, too, we need to take care not to assume that a postnatally depressed mother is bound to have a partner who is equally depressed, or that having a baby is just as likely to impact on either or both partners in a way that produces depression. Take the reaction of this father to his wife's depression, which was one of stoical acceptance – though this didn't mean he was unresponsive or uncaring towards her:

'I can't actually remember when I realized R was depressed – it just seemed to me that she was having a hard time adapting to the change in circumstances. I mean, she'd had a bad time at the birth, and then breastfeeding went wrong and she was upset at having to give the baby bottles. I know she was also affected by the fact we didn't know many people nearby. I just figured she wasn't too good at coping. I think we're quite different faced with this sort of thing. I tend to stay calm when things change. I think women have moods, and there's not much you can do about it – just accept it. You go on learning and living. She's fine, mostly, these days, though she says she would like to get back to normal one day. But I don't think there can be any "back to normal" when you have small children. It changes you, and your life, for ever.'

Another study examined the impact on the father and his relationship with the mother as a result of postnatal depression. 'The men experienced fear, confusion, and much concern for their spouses, and felt unable to help them in overcoming PND. The inability to "fix the problem" created frustration and anger. The majority of the respondents reported that they made many sacrifices to hold the relationship and the family together.'[8]

Sex and Postnatal Depression

'When things in your life just aren't right,' said a friend who is an experienced relationships counsellor, 'you can guarantee they're even worse in your bedroom.'

She might have altered 'even worse' to 'non-existent' when it comes to postnatal depression.

Postnatally-depressed women, at best, can't be bothered about sex. Like the woman in the old joke who says, 'well, all right then, I suppose so ... but for God's sake try not to wake me up when you're doing it,' sheer exhaustion precludes it, and any sexual feelings just seem buried beneath layers of nappies, broken nights, social pressures and the sound of a baby screaming.

> 'It seemed such a waste – here we had two safe hours to ourselves when my mother took the baby one Sunday afternoon, and all he wanted to use it for was sex ... all I could think of to do was sleep.'

At worst, there is a revulsion about sex, perhaps associated with a bad birth experience when a woman has felt mauled and even abused. Or perhaps the lack of self-esteem that goes with depression is the over-riding factor.

> 'Sex was a non-thing for us for ages. The thought that someone would want me was disgusting.'

If you've had sexual feelings before, and your relationship remains strong, your desires will come back when the depression recedes. You may need to give your libido a kickstart – one mother I spoke to deliberately got out a raunchy video, and got things going that way by watching it with her husband. You need to keep the channels of physical, sensual communication open if you can. Touch, stroke, hug, caress, kiss – even if you have to explain to your partner that you don't want it to go any further just yet.

The Rest of the Family

We've already discussed how childhood experiences of being parented are worth exploring in therapy and counselling for postnatal depression (see page 35).

What about the current effect on the depressed mother's present relationships with her family, however? Or on her in-laws?

Mothers who are depressed can sometimes get a lot of support from their families. That can be very demanding for those families, and distressing for a grandmother, who may need to be very strong while coping with her own sadness at seeing someone she loves in such turmoil.

I heard from a number of new mothers who'd moved back into the old family home – one woman crossed the world to do so, and stayed for several weeks. There is such a powerful need to be mothered oneself at this time, and going 'home' can be an effective way to meet this need. Living with your mum in her house means life can be simplified. Depressed mothers find any sort of decision-making to be very difficult – staying with someone else takes a lot of that away.

'My mum took two months off work to look after me. She just got on with things. I didn't have to ask her to do anything.'

'I'd been living away from home for 17 years when I had my baby. It had never bothered me before, but having a baby makes a difference. It hits you just how much you need your mum and how isolated you are.'

Grandmothers sometimes seem to know something's wrong – maybe comparing their own experiences to their daughter's.

A grandmother told me,

'There is a problem of depression in our family, especially among the women. My own mother, and her sisters, suffered from it, and I recognize the tendency in myself too. I knew my daughter was going through a bad time after her babies were born, but in fact she was very open about it, anyway. She was easily moved to tears, especially if we had a small disagreement – she was just generally more fragile. And she looked so very tired. I remember a few days after her second baby she was extremely low – she cried and cried as if her heart would break.'

Said a daughter,

'My mum told me she could see I was very good at covering up, but there was still, to her, clear signs that things weren't right.'

One mother – writing in the Association for Postnatal Illness newsletter in 1996 – who suffered two bouts of postnatal depression, one severe enough to send her to hospital six times in two years, a violent attack from her husband, divorce, a miscarriage after a disastrous 'rebound' relationship, and massive debt problems, found her only consistent help and comfort came from her parents:

'... my mum and dad were great and supported me from the start ... over the years I have matured and I have come to realize that consistency and hard work can help you recover, and that one important factor in recovery is family support and love.'

The grandmother quoted earlier felt she helped most by helping in the house where she could, by listening, by being accepting, and by

> 'just standing behind her. She knows I love her, she knows I don't try to tell her what to do, and I would never criticize the way she brings up her children. However, when she became depressed after her second baby, I did suggest she get help more quickly than she had done the first time, and she did so.'

It's not all good news. Some parents and in-laws are not around, because they have died, or they just aren't able to offer help, because of distance, work or other caring commitments, lack of cash, their own emotional problems, disability.

If there are clashes and bitterness, some grandparents are probably best out of the way. That's also the case if the mother feels she can't ever be frank about her problems, or if she always has to be the peacemaker.

> 'Ironically, it was a huge family row when I just went totally loopy with rage that forced me to seek help for my depression. But I had to ask my parents to stay away in the end – on medical grounds, to be honest. They are just not conducive to mental health.'

NCT teacher Jeanne Langford asked mothers in an antenatal class what they wanted from their mothers and mothers-in-law after the birth, and what experienced mothers had found helpful before. In more supportive societies than ours, what they ask for would be taken for granted coming from a range of family and friends. Here's some of their 'wish list':

- My mother could help by leaving me holding the baby while she does the washing up.
- I want my mother to be sensitive to my needs at the time   I might want help and support or I might want to be left alone.
- My mother stays for two weeks and runs the house and helps with the other children. She is ideal for this role because she is very discreet and manages to blend into the household without disturbing it too much.
- My mother-in-law could see the baby and cook a meal once a week.
- I would like my mother-in-law to give practical help if requested, and advice, if requested.
- I appreciate her shopping for baby clothes and equipment I can't get out and buy.

Questions and Answers

Q. ARE WOMEN WHO DON'T HAVE A PERMANENT PARTNER MORE LIKELY TO SUFFER POSTNATAL DEPRESSION?

A. Yes. But having an unhappy relationship with a partner is also a risk factor. Women who have a poor relationship with their own mothers are more likely to suffer, too, as are women who don't have any close friend to talk to. Close, confiding relationships are protective of a new mother, and any woman who is lonely and isolated, or living in an unhappy partnership, may need more support after the birth of her baby.

References for Chapter Three

1 C.G. Ballard *et al*. Prevalence of postnatal psychiatric morbidity in mothers and fathers. *British Journal of Psychiatry*, June 1994.

2 J. Milgrom, P. McCloud. Parenting stress and postnatal depression. *Stress Medicine*, July 1996.

3 P. Noller et al. A longitudinal study of conflict in early marriage. *Journal of Social and Personal Relationships*, Vol. 11, 233–252, 1994.

4 M.E.G. Areias *et al*. Comparative incidence of depression in women and men during pregnancy and after childbirth. *British Journal of Psychiatry*, July 1996.

5 Christchurch Postnatal Survey, reported in *Parents Centres New Zealand*, August/September 1995.

6 Suggested by Dr Melanie Epstein at CPHVA conference, Postnatal depression: a primary health care challenge. Newcastle upon Tyne, July 1997.

7 S. Matthey *et al*. Validation of the Edinburgh Postnatal Depression Scale for men, and comparison of item endorsement with their partners. *Journal of Affective Disorders*, May 2001.

8 M. Meighan *et al*. Living with postpartum depression: the father's experience. *American Journal Maternal and Child Nursing*, July–August 1999.

5

Four Stories

'Babies shatter complacency. They reveal your identity as you
never knew yourself before. They force you to see the world
in a new way. They produce a fresh challenge every day.'

Writer Sheila Kitzinger's characteristically accurate assessment of
the effect of a new baby – from her book *The Year After Childbirth*
(Oxford University Press, 1994) – shows just how great the impact
of new parenthood can be. Postnatal depression may be one of
the greatest 'fresh challenges' that babies bring, forcing a new view
of the world upon so many mothers and fathers. Yet no single experience of it is the same as another's. Here are four experiences, which
show how uniquely each mother is affected by existing expectations,
family circumstances, treatments and outcomes.

Michael and Sue's story (pages 94-99) is recounted in two 'his
and hers' parts, which is how it was told to me, on two separate interviews, held a week apart. Neither knew what the other had said to
me. Both their versions of the same experience and sequence of events
are fascinating, honest and revealing.

Annie

Two children, daughter Rosa, aged four, son Tom, aged three

'Everything went fine with Rosa – I can remember people said "oh, Annie, you're so good at this!"

'It was so different with Tom. We were moving house at the time, and I was under a lot of pressure. We were living in rented accommodation, and Tom was actually born there – I had wanted a home delivery and it was a really good birth. Three hours later, I was up and about, doing things.

'Then, it all started. I felt so tired. A week after the birth I left a message on my mum's answering machine saying "I just don't want this baby in the house". I felt inadequate, and guilty for feeling like that. I couldn't make any decisions about anything.

'I was actually very afraid I would hurt the children. Tom was such a pain – once I actually threw him down into the cot I was so cross with him. I wanted a different baby – I didn't want him. I thought he could read my mind. I'd think "you know I hate you!"

'I tried to explain my behaviour to myself by saying I was exhausted, and at three months I went to the doctor to ask for sleeping pills. He told me he wouldn't prescribe anything while I was still breastfeeding. Yes, I was still feeding, amazingly – it was the one thing that linked me to the baby.

'To other people it looked as though I was coping. My mum was so worried, she rang the midwife and asked what to do. The midwife was very good, and she arranged for the doctor to come and see me at home. He prescribed anti-depressants but he said I would have to stop feeding –

the way he put it, the baby needed me to be happy more than he needed my milk [see page 71 – stopping breastfeeding is not inevitable].

'It took a fortnight for the pills to work, and to feel I was gradually getting better. The heavy, sluggish feeling I'd had began to lift. I started counselling – arranged by the doctor – when Tom was five months old and I found that very helpful.

'It's very gradual, and I had some setbacks. Tom was a difficult baby. He cried a lot, and as he got older he became aggressive and sleepless. He developed eczema. I had a furious row with my mother about the way he was behaving, though we made up afterwards. My husband was a great support to me, but I found it upsetting that some people among our friends and family didn't like me to use the word "depression" – apparently it made them feel uncomfortable. Tough. The more people that realize it could happen to them, or anyone they know, the better.

'My confidence came back when Tom was about a year old, and I came off antidepressants when he was 14 months. By then, I really loved both the children, and I feel I'm in the middle of a love affair with Tom, trying to make up for lost time!

'I have learnt so much from the whole experience. I began to do part-time work when I came off the pills, and I felt I'd found my equilibrium again. Counselling has made me realize my tendency to put pressure on myself. I was determined that Rosa wouldn't miss out on anything, despite the fact I had a new baby to look after. I found it so hard to abandon any job or family task and say "oh, I give up. Someone else can do this." Inside I was screaming, "what about me?" You end up not having a "me" in amongst everyone else's demands.'

Joy

One child, Ben, aged two and a half

'The whole thing started very quickly and suddenly. Just two days after Ben's birth, I started to cry and cry, and I couldn't stop. I didn't think I was ill, or anything. I just couldn't get a grip on things. I felt terrible, and everyone around me was pretty frightened. They could see this wasn't just three-day blues or anything trivial. I was in a desperate state – and the days went on and I was just as bad.

'I had a terrible fear I would harm myself. I pictured myself doing it, with a knife. I knew I wouldn't harm Ben. I just didn't feel capable of looking after him. I wasn't worth anything.

'My husband Tony is in the army, and he was allowed to extend his leave. We both went to stay with his mum, as there was no way he could even leave me for a few minutes on my own. I was incapable of making any sort of decision. I had thought I would breastfeed, but there was no way I could have done it. I could never have got my act together to relate to the baby in any way, or put him on the breast – it seemed an impossible idea to me. So it was bottles, but they had their problems. I worried that the bottles would get contaminated, and I wouldn't even let Tony go anywhere near them. I was so sure he'd contaminate them. I wouldn't let Tony bottle feed Ben. I thought he would choke him and it would be my fault. But I couldn't decide when Ben needed feeding. I couldn't even decide when to change his nappy.

'The doctor prescribed antidepressants, and the community psychiatric nurse visited. She came every day for ages, and then she thought she could leave it for a couple of days to see how I got on. I had a relapse, when I became overwhelmed with anxiety. Then I pulled myself back up, and I looked as if I was coping better.

'I still had scary thoughts, but I kept them to myself. If I saw a poster on cot death, I'd think it was targeted at me. It took me a year to totally relax about bottles. But in the end I did, and I went back to work feeling as if I was taking a massive step towards normality. Work helped – it really brought me into contact with the "real" world, and it took my mind off my negative thoughts.

'I look back, and I think the depression started when I was pregnant. I'd had a threatened miscarriage, and from then on I was so worried all the time. These days, I am still on medication, but I work and enjoy Ben, and most of the time I suppose I'm okay. We have happy times as a family, and a good laugh on occasions. Tony just accepts me the way I am, and doesn't complain. But I am different. I wish I was back to the person I used to be – carefree, lighthearted...

'I have a lot more sympathy with people who have depression nowadays. I would never want to go through the experience again, and in fact I've been sterilized to make sure I don't.

'You know, even when the worst of the illness had passed, I was still frightened, and I was lonely. Most people don't know the half of what you're going through. You put on a front.'

Yolanda

One child Ellie, aged two

'I didn't realize for ages and ages that I was depressed. I know I was very tearful at times, and I felt I wasn't coping the way I should be, and I used to resent the baby's cries and her demands ... and she was very demanding! But I kept it all to myself, like a guilty secret. I didn't think I could tell anyone what I really felt about being a mum.

'I'd had a good pregnancy. I had hoped to give birth at home, but she went two weeks overdue, and I was advised to go into hospital for an induction. I suppose I was a bit disappointed that things weren't going to go to plan but it wasn't a major setback. The whole thing went well. It only lasted four and a half hours, and the pain was bearable. I used a TENS machine to relieve the pain [TENS – transcutaneous nerve stimulation – is a simple form of pain relief, which delivers a faint electric current via a small black box worn against the body]. The staff were great, and explained everything. I was in control, and I felt good. Afterwards I was overjoyed.

'Breastfeeding went well, though there were days when Ellie fed constantly. It was very hot that summer, and she seemed to need to be on the breast the whole time. She didn't sleep very much, either in the day or the night.

'There were days and days when I was totally on my own with her, when my husband was working away.

'My health visitor was nice, though a bit limited. She didn't know much about breastfeeding, and made some critical remarks about Ellie not gaining weight according to the chart.

I found that very undermining, and it's stuck with me, so I must have taken it to heart. I changed health visitors, as a result of that. The next one was better. She recognized loneliness, and she said I should go along to a play morning at the church hall. I managed to pluck up the courage and go. It was truly awful. No one spoke to me. I didn't want to go again, but I made myself. I told myself it would be worth sticking at, and I knew I desperately needed to get out of the house.

'Things struggled on. I never complained. My husband's teenage sons from his first marriage stayed with us every weekend – and they never lifted a finger. I felt I had to show my husband I didn't resent them a bit, and I could easily look after them as well as a tiny baby. The strain started to show eventually, though. I couldn't watch anything sad on the nine o'clock news. I would just cry.

'Then one day I really blew my top at my husband and his younger son over something. I remember the look on their faces. They were so shocked. They'd seen me tearful before, but not this. I felt all my anger and resentment bubble over.

'It made a difference. I felt my husband started to become more understanding and he took my co-operation with the boys far less for granted. Of course things didn't magically improve overnight. It took time, but once I'd acknowledged that things weren't perfect, I was on the way to getting better. I didn't feel I needed pills, or any formal outside help – just support at home.

'Gradually, I became more confident about talking to other people at meetings like the play morning, and I could feel the depression was lifting. I would say I am fully recovered now.'

Sue and Michael

Three children, Peter aged four, Matthew aged three and Freddie aged 20 months

Sue

'I was fine after Peter and Matthew were born. Then with Freddie I became pretty depressed in pregnancy. We'd moved to Australia. Michael wasn't working full-time and I was half a world away from my family. I was doing a PhD and didn't get on with my supervisor. I was melting in the heat. Then we heard that the tenants in our house in the UK had done a bunk without paying any rent. It wasn't the ideal time to have a third baby.

'My in-laws came out for a holiday, and stayed with us – but there wasn't really enough room, and life just got more and more pressured.

'Freddie was born, and for two days I was on a high. Then I came down to earth, realizing it was all too much. I just couldn't cope. Michael told me I could, and it would be all right – I felt he was so unsupportive. I was still supposed to be continuing with the PhD and I went into the university with Freddie when he was just six days old. I didn't feel I could take any time off.

'Our money situation was dire. We were up to the limit on our credit cards. I went into the shop one morning for bread to give the children breakfast and the shop refused my credit card. I looked in my purse and I had nothing – not a bean. I couldn't even buy bread to feed my kids. I came home and broke down, crying.

'The GP said I had postnatal depression, and so did the midwife. The GP recommended medication. Michael was awful. He recommended a walk. He thought he could bully me out of it. All I wanted was a month off – he said no.

'I started taking medication anyway, but it was horrible stuff that made me drowsy. I couldn't drive with it, but I stayed with it. I continued breastfeeding until Freddie was five months, but I didn't really enjoy it. He needed such a lot of feeding – I felt shrivelled. I kept thinking of that daft line from *Wayne's World* – "he's sucking my will to live." That's just how it felt. There were days I'd look at him and think "I don't want to feed you. I don't even want to pick you up. You might need a nappy change and I can't cope."

'When he was two months old I'd had enough. I bought an air ticket (which we couldn't afford) and came home to my mum in the UK. 27 hours in a plane with a baby and two toddlers ... imagine. I landed, and found my grandmother had just died, so I couldn't stay with mum, as she was arranging the funeral and so on. I had to stay with my sister, but that didn't work, as she and her husband were in the middle of rehearsals for some amateur dramatics thing they were involved with, and they left me looking after their daughter as well as my own three.

'At one point when I was there, I looked at Freddie lying in his Moses basket and came so close to smothering him. I kept thinking, "it's all his fault. If it wasn't for him, none of this would be the way it is."

'After a week, I went to my mum's and things seemed better at first. I was still on medication, but I felt at last someone was looking after me. Then after two months, I realized I couldn't go back to Australia. I just couldn't face it. I broke down completely. Mum's GP saw me, and called in a psychiatrist.

He asked me if I wanted to go into hospital, and I said no. He put me on some stronger medication. He also got a social worker to see me, as I was so angry and impatient with the kids. She was hopeless – drippy and pathetic. But she must have decided there was nothing really to worry about – the children were fine and mum was there the whole time.

'A family friend who was a trained counsellor talked to me, and she was good. I still felt dreadful, but people around me were being very supportive and caring. No one was putting any pressure on me to go back to Australia – except Michael. He decided to come out and see me. The day he arrived was my lowest point. I was feeling so terrible, and he was so bright and energetic, full of plans to cart us all off to the USA now, as he'd had a job offer. I just thought ..."Whaaaat?????" I couldn't believe he could be so dense and unhelpful. Crossing the road was a major expedition to me, and here he was, going on about America...

'I went to my room and lay down and cried and cried. My husband didn't need me. My kids were better off with my mum. What was the point in carrying on? I told God, "if you don't show me someone needs me, I'm going out into the road to wait for a milk tanker to mow me down."

'I went downstairs, ready to go out the door. Mum had made the children boiled eggs, and Peter had eaten his. He'd turned it over in the egg cup to make it look whole again – you know, that joke all children love. He saw me, and said delightedly, "Mummy, Mummy, look ... I've got a new egg!" He needed me to laugh with him. I realized I was wanted. I stayed in the house.

'Michael apologized for his plans, and things got a little better. We decided to stay in the UK for the time being. We moved back to our own house, and I started to look for a job. When Michael had to go away for work interviews, I made sure someone else was in the house with me. I stayed on medication – I did for a year, then came off slowly.

'Michael got a job, and the summer was okay – he was made redundant after a couple of months, though. We managed to cope, even so, and he found something else.

'The worst of the depression is long over, and I have a part-time teaching job.

'I feel much better about Freddie – I love him, he's wonderful! I grieve for those six months I lost with him.'

Michael

'I remember one day shortly before Freddie's birth, I got a phone call from Sue. She was distraught. She was worried about me – I had been feeling depressed for a couple of years, mainly because it was so difficult for me to get a permanent job. Anyway, she was upset and I came home. I found she was talking to a counsellor, and she was very weepy. That was the first real sign I had that Sue was feeling low. We had a bad couple of months around the time Freddie was born. But I didn't think there was anything really, well, pathological about what Sue was feeling. She's not the most phlegmatic of people at the best of times, and she got things out of proportion. I thought the best thing for her, for us, would be to try to get back to normal. I wanted Sue to continue with her studying. She'd enjoyed it before – going into the university gave her a break from the demands of small children, and it was something she could fit in round their needs. But she told me things were totally different, and she couldn't face it. So I agreed she might benefit from a short break.

'When things got a bit better she just didn't see it. She stayed negative. She wouldn't confide in me, and kept it all inside – it was frustrating to see, when I still believed that together, we could overcome challenges. I was disappointed in her, I suppose. She seemed so miserable all the time.

'I remember once she made a huge thing about the shop not accepting her credit card, and she had to come home without any shopping. But she'd used the wrong card, that was all. We had a cash flow problem, true, but we were never so short we couldn't actually eat. I didn't resent her feeling like that, but I was hurt that she wouldn't even try to see things my way and maybe feel a bit better about our life together.

'She pinned her hopes on coming to England, but I gather the journey was a nightmare, and then when she got there she found her grandmother had died. She was by then in a full-blown depressive breakdown.

'I was so worried about her – what could I do? But there I was, on the other side of the world ... I felt helpless. When I phoned she sounded peculiar, she'd forget previous conversations and things she'd said the previous day, and it was quite scary. She told me the shrink had put her on some mega-medication, and that worried me.

'Then there seemed to be this idea that it was all my fault. My parents, her parents, certainly seemed to think so. My stepfather said he was ashamed of me. He seemed to have taken on the role of being Sue's spokesperson. I was losing my role in Sue's and my relationship. I knew I wasn't exactly golden boy before – Sue's parents had never wanted her to marry at 19, or to go to Australia – but we got on okay most of the time before this.

'I decided the best thing for me to do was to come home to see her so I scraped up enough cash by borrowing yet again.

When I saw her I was so shocked. She looked terrible. She was so haggard. Honestly, her face was, I don't know, the only way I can describe it is "pale black".

'I'd come over with the idea of cheering her up. I'd been offered a new job in Florida, and I thought it would be a fresh start for all of us, but she was so angry, negative and irrational I could see I wasn't getting anywhere.

'I was desperate. She didn't seem to care about our relationship at all. My in-laws definitely blamed me – they more or less told me I'd reduced Sue to this awful state and then dumped her on a plane to be sorted out by her mum and dad.

'I realized I would have to think in terms of staying in the UK, and once I told her my thoughts, things started to improve. We moved into our house again, and she stopped seeing me as the bogey man. I started earning regular money, and we found a church we liked – that's important to Sue as she needs the support.

'Sue needs a meaningful vision, I think, of what life could be like, and she's getting that back. She is still fragile, and I try to push her to be more positive but I don't get very far. She sometimes gets sulky, and I think she uses the experience of depression as a crutch – it's a bit disappointing. But I know it must be really frightening to think you might go back to being tempted to kill yourself …

'The good thing is I feel we do still have a marriage and we're loyal and committed to each other. She hasn't blamed me in the long term. Now we have to see where we go from here.'

6

What About the Baby?

'I felt so detached from her…sometimes I'd spend an entire day singing every nursery rhyme I could think of, and other days I wouldn't talk to her at all.'

Life, and experience, is different for the baby whose mother is depressed. The effects of depression have an impact on the baby, in ways we are beginning to understand and to measure. The baby's development, behaviour and possibly even intelligence are changed.

It's not known how long the effects might last, but in some studies they can be clearly seen at primary school age. It appears that depression does influence the mother's relationship with her baby, not only during her depression, but also afterwards when she has recovered … sometimes long afterwards.

Mothers who've been depressed find this quite disturbing – understandably. Some, like the mother quoted at the start of this chapter, who spoke to *Prima Baby* magazine for the Winter 1997/98 issue, look back and remember quite clearly how they reacted to their babies – but they expect to be able to put the experience behind them. They feel 'blamed', and disappointed, too, that the experience still has a knock-on effect on their child.

I was at a large meeting of health professionals in the summer of 1997, when the subject of long-term effects came up. There was a frisson around the lecture theatre. Many of the 100 or so attendees had had postnatal depression themselves – when a show of hands had been asked for earlier, I estimated the rate was about a third. A number of people who'd raised their hands before then stood up and reassured the rest of the audience that their children were fine and their relationship with their children was fine, too – and while of course individual cases can't be predicted, bland and general reassurance is not helpful.

The growing amount of research into this area reinforces the principle that postnatal depression matters, and a mother who suffers from it deserves attention, and help – doubly so, as her baby reaps the consequences.

As Professor Lynne Murray, one of the pioneers in this area, told the *Observer* newspaper in October 1997, 'motherhood is very undervalued in our society – what our work shows is that mothering is of vital importance to our children's future and well-being, and therefore requires society's fullest support'. It's not fair to anyone to pretend otherwise.

So far, studies done on the interactions of depressed mothers and their babies show that depressed mothers:

❑ may have more difficulty than well mothers in settling, soothing and managing demands for attention

❑ may appear withdrawn and 'disengaged' with their babies, and flat and unresponsive to their 'cues' of smiles or sounds

❑ may sometimes handle their babies rather roughly, speak angrily and don't seem to know when the baby needs careful, gentler handling

❑   may veer between the two responses – unresponsive and over-responsive.

❑   may seem less in tune with their babies' emotional and social needs.

The studies that came up with these findings took place when the babies were between two and six months old.[1]

Later on, researchers have studied toddlers and older children in various projects. For example, in programmes based at the Winnicott Research Unit, Reading University, and in London, the same two groups of mothers and children have been tracked since the mid-1980s.

The results[2] have shown that children of mothers who've been depressed are more likely than other children to:

❑   show signs of insecurity at 12 months and 18 months
❑   score worse on some intelligence tests at 18 months
❑   show mild behaviour difficulties at 18 months, and at four years
❑   score less well on some intelligence tests at four years (boys only)
❑   show 'significantly lower IQ scores' at age 11 (especially in boys)[3].

Not all the studies confirm each other, and it's clear we have a lot to learn. So far, it appears that boys whose mothers have been depressed are more likely to be difficult, disruptive and 'challenging'. Girls are more likely to be eager to please, helpful and compliant – maybe too compliant, with maybe too great a need to please, suggested education writer Victoria Neumark in *The Times Educational Supplement* in June 1997, when assessing the possible interpretations of the findings.

Could it be that these patterns of behaviour have been learnt years ago? Victoria Neumark, looking at the Winnicott Research Unit's fieldwork, thinks about the way boys and girls react differently to the depressed interactions of their mothers, when they are just two months old.

Video clips show mothers not 'in sync' with their babies, not responding to their babies' attempts to communicate. 'Girl and boy babies alike are puzzled by this pattern, but whereas the girls would tend after a few vain efforts to revive the conversation, to give up, the boys would bellow and strain.'

She speculates: 'is it too fanciful to suppose that babies and children somehow feel responsible for their mother's sadness and either try to make it up to them (the girls) or to distract them from it (the boys)?'

The Winnicott's Professor Lynne Murray is more guarded. She says the study does not yet show whether the difference between girls and boys was because mothers find it easier to care for their daughters than their sons, or it could just be that girls are more able to let the effects of depression bounce off them ... and maybe that in itself could be an early indicator of other difficulties.

So Where's the Link?

For most researchers, it's those early depressed interactions, or lack of them, that cause the longer-term effects, shown in studies on babies, toddlers and children. Some mothers are depressed yet relate well and communicate with their babies – and their babies don't develop any differently from the babies of mothers who are well. So it's not the depression itself that has the effect, but the communication problems it brings about in the mother.

Good social conditions can go some way to reduce those longer-term effects, says the research. As Professor Murray points out, 'it seems that good circumstances can help buffer any negative impact. When we think about possible implications of depression for child cognitive development, therefore, we need to take into account the kind of environment the family has. We should be particularly aware if the family is from very deprived circumstances, as the risks are much greater for those children[4].'

Other members of the family have an important role to play as caregivers and communicators when the mother is unable to attach because of depression. Taking postnatal depression seriously because of the potential effect on babies should not be used to make depressed mothers feel even worse – communication and relationships are not inevitably affected adversely, and long-term effects do not occur in the majority. Babies, as well as mothers, can make up for 'lost time'.

One way of short-circuiting the effect could be to help and support mothers before they get severely depressed, and to treat them with their babies. The right sort of health visitor support can head off behavioural problems[5], but as the *Observer* points out, 'this necessary work is being recognized just as cash-strapped health authorities are axing health visitors and other front-line services'.

What Mothers Feel About Their Babies

Mothers who are depressed almost always care perfectly adequately for their babies in a physical sense, unless they are suffering very severely, or have puerperal psychosis. This may take a huge effort, and for a few, it may even be at the expense of their own personal care – one mother told me she wore the same tatty old pair of leggings for weeks because she just couldn't decide to change them, and what to wear instead if she did.

But their emotional feelings towards their babies cover a range. Some depressed mothers love their babies from the very start, or grow to love them within a short time. Others are indifferent, or actively resentful. A few find they have thoughts of harming their baby. Almost always, however, women recognize these feelings as misplaced, and the very fact they have these thoughts is another powerful source of distress.

'I'd loved my baby immediately after the birth, but I didn't seem to have the energy for love now. I wanted to run away, to forget I'd ever had her.'

'I'd be so furious with him for wanting extra feeds or sleeping at the "wrong time", I'd cry and cry and cry. I felt desperate, trapped, a victim of this tyrannical baby.'

'I just didn't like her – I felt I could have left her on the bus and not been bothered.'

'One day I threw him down into the cot, really roughly, and then felt dreadful – how could I feel so horrible towards him? He was only a tiny, helpless baby – but I didn't feel he was mine.'

'My feelings towards the baby were awful. Before I did anything too horrendous, I called Chris and begged him to come home. As soon as he arrived I left the house and ran to my mother's. I cried in pain. Never, never was I going to harm my children.'

Postnatal depression is one of the major causes of problems with 'attachment', which is when a mother feels very little emotional connection between herself and her baby. The study of why and how mothers don't connect with their babies is relatively new, but depression can make the mother emotionally unavailable, and so a loving relationship doesn't develop as it would otherwise.[6]

Vicky was a mother of twins, featured on BBC TV's QED series *Challenging Children* in the summer of 1997.

She was very depressed, and she was shown sitting on the floor in a corner of her kitchen, almost hiding from her boy-girl, eight-month-old twins. The film also showed her trying so hard to relate to them, to do what they wanted, to cuddle and play, to talk, to sing, swinging them round, spoonfeed them with their dinner – and getting nowhere. Whatever she did, the babies cried and whined. When she held them or swung them, they writhed and wriggled to be put down. Just who was the most miserable – Vicky or her twins? It was a toss-up.

In a poignant sequence of film, we saw Vicky gradually getting better, as she was helped by one-to-one counselling about her depression, and supportive guidance on interacting with the twins. Her ability to relate to them improved at the same time as her depression lifted – it seemed a closely-linked process.

We know that non-depressed as well as depressed mothers may take a while to feel 'bonded' to their baby, and it doesn't always mean that things will become as sad and difficult as they were with Vicky. The process of feeling close to your baby can be affected by a number of factors:

- ❏ your own health – if you're not well, or totally exhausted, you may not yet relate to your baby
- ❏ a difficult birth
- ❏ separation from your baby, for example, if your baby needs to spend time in special care
- ❏ disappointment at the sex of your baby
- ❏ your own personality.

It's also affected by the personality of the baby – babies are real people with different characteristics, and some of them are easier to relate to at first. Murray and her researchers found that your attachment to your baby is a two-way street, with the baby's input and responses of vital importance.[7]

Older Children

The baby's older brothers and sisters may also feel the effect of the mother's depression. It's as if in their depressed state, mothers find it impossible to care for more than one child at a time.

> 'I pushed my daughter and husband away. It was like I just wanted to take care of the baby and ... the rest of you should go away, because I can't deal with the rest of it.'[8]

Older children may need extra attention and extra shows of affection from other members of the family while their mum is depressed, and when she's recovering, they may need reassurance through your words (if they're old enough to understand) and your actions, that things will soon get better.

Breastfeeding and Postnatal Depression

You'll sometimes hear conflicting advice about breastfeeding and postnatal depression.

On the one hand, you may hear you have to be very confident, and relaxed, to breastfeed or the milk won't flow.

On the other, you're told that breastfeeding's great for you if you have a tendency to get uptight, as the hormonal effects are so relaxing...

Speaking purely biologically, both views could be correct.

Some women do find their let-down (the reflex that causes the milk to be released from within the breast and to travel down the ducts to the nipple) is temporarily affected by severe emotional stress or crisis. And it's also true that feel-good endorphins (types of chemicals) are released into your bloodstream when you breast-feed.[9]

Neither of those phenomena has any real bearing on whether or not you are likely to have a good breastfeeding experience, however. There's certainly no evidence that mothers who are of a nervous or anxious character should avoid breastfeeding.

Yet there are links between postnatal well-being and breastfeeding. One major overview of the issue looked at most of the recent studies of the topic.[10] The authors concluded that breastfeeding mothers with normal hormone levels (in particular, of prolactin, the milk-making hormone, and progesterone), plus good social support, have better adjustment to their new life as a mother, greater confidence and less anxiety than bottle-feeders. Breastfeeding does not increase the chance of postnatal depression, and successful breastfeeding may actually protect against depression for some women.

I've emphasized the 'successful' as it seems clear that unhappy breastfeeding and depression are closely linked.

My experience as a breastfeeding counsellor, my interviews with mothers and evidence from studies looking at the way depressed mothers feed, indicate that depressed mothers find some difficulty with the necessary 'tuning in' to their baby's needs. This may have a lot to do with confidence and self-esteem – both important in protecting against depression.

Then, when breastfeeding goes wrong, for whatever reason (sore nipples, lack of confidence in it, mastitis and so on), it's such a confidence-drainer. Women can feel failures if they don't manage to breastfeed – and that in itself may increase their susceptibility to postnatal depression. But which comes first – the unhappy breast-feeding, or the depression? I suspect it could be either.

However, any mother who wants to breastfeed should be given the right information and support with which to do it happily – in the knowledge that doing so she'll be a happier, more confident mother with a baby who's getting the best nutritional start in life. There is evidence that breastfeeding can 'intervene' and lessen some of the risks to the baby of depression – Cardiff researchers discovered that 'breastfeeding exerted its own [positive] influence on Verbal IQ and appeared to mediate the link with mathematical ability' in children aged 11, whose mothers had been postnatally depressed.[11]

But women who don't manage to breastfeed, or decide it's not for them, need and deserve support and acceptance, just as much as anyone else who's breastfeeding with or without problems.

If you end up bottle-feeding, you might feel sad – even if that sadness is mixed with relief that you don't have to struggle any more. Unhappy breastfeeding is a struggle. You might be helped by speaking to a breastfeeding counsellor, who can help you talk through your feelings, understand better what happened, and support you in whatever choice you've made. Breastfeeding is undoubtedly the best way of feeding a baby – but it's not the only good way of mothering a baby.

What Mothers Say About Breastfeeding

'Despite all the help I got with breastfeeding, she just wouldn't latch on. I had to change to formula, and I felt like a great big failure.'

'Once he was on half breast and half bottles, I realized I was feeling much stronger, less physically exhausted and more stable emotionally ... as the last weeks of breastfeeding went by, I'd have attacks of conscience and I knew I was losing something precious and intimate with Jack. But once it was over, I never missed it.'

'I didn't have much confidence in my ability to breastfeed, but it went all right ... he thrived on it, and that made me feel here's one thing I'm getting right ...'

'To me, it was really important to breastfeed. I got blocked ducts, and cracked nipples, but I would have felt even more depressed if I'd stopped.'

'Breastfeeding kept us together. I didn't like my baby one bit – so I had to hang on to the feeding as the one and only link I had with her.'

'Breastfeeding was a disaster for me. I had desperately wanted to breastfeed but I developed sore nipples early on. The staff kept saying "she's well-positioned so it's not that," but I knew she wasn't. I gave up in despair, and I am sure that contributed to my breakdown.'

'I feel my depression was hormonal, as it descended on me when I stopped feeding at nine months.'

'The doctor told me I had to take the tablets, and I had to stop breastfeeding. The drugs knocked me sideways – I felt I'd been hit by a sledgehammer. I felt so upset at having handed over my life to this stupid doctor who knew nothing. I kept thinking, "if I hadn't listened to her, I would have still been feeding". This is something I will always regret.'

'James completely rejected the breast and not even the breast-feeding counsellor could advise, so I reluctantly resorted to the bottle. We're made to feel failures if we end up bottle feeding and this certainly contributed to my feelings of inadequacy.'

Questions and Answers

Q. I HAD POSTNATAL DEPRESSION VERY SEVERELY WHEN MY SON WAS BORN THREE YEARS AGO. MY SON IS NOW HAPPY AND HEALTHY, AND WE HAVE A LOVING RELATIONSHIP WITH EACH OTHER. HE HAS SETTLED IN WELL AT HIS NURSERY SCHOOL, AND HE LIKES DOING ALL THE THINGS OTHER THREE-YEAR-OLDS LIKE DOING ... BUT I CAN'T STOP WONDERING IF MY DEPRESSION HAS AFFECTED HIM IN SOME WAY. I FEEL SO GUILTY ABOUT IT, AND ABOUT THE WAY I REALLY DIDN'T LOVE HIM WHEN HE WAS TINY.

A. Guilt is an occupational hazard of being a mother. All of us, depressed or not, can feel it at times. It springs from our deep love for our children, and our desire that they have a fulfilled, carefree life.

Your depression was not your fault. Start by 'forgiving' yourself and liking yourself again. The feelings of loss you have for those first few months of your baby's life are strong, and normal. Postnatal depression has been described as a thief, robbing mothers of the intimacy with their children.

You can't wipe out what happened – but you can focus on the here and now. This might mean doing your best to enjoy your little boy, spending time with him when you can give him your full attention, and taking pleasure from the fact that he is clearly happy and well-adjusted at home and outside it.

Statistics and research into any subject can never allow us to describe or predict individual behaviour or experience. In the end, you are the one observing your son, and this should be your reassurance that you have nothing to worry about.

Q. I WAS SO SCARED WHEN I WAS DEPRESSED THAT MY BABY WOULD BE TAKEN INTO CARE – EVEN THOUGH I NEVER HARMED HIM. WAS I RIGHT TO WORRY?

A. It is highly unlikely the baby of a depressed mother would be considered to be at risk unless the mother showed signs she felt violent towards him, or had already done something violent like slapping or shaking. Having a violent thought which is instantly checked and overcome is not the same. Your baby would not be taken into care unless your depression was so severe and disabling you were unable to look after him, and there was no other close person (your partner or your mother, for example) available to take over.

References for Chapter Six

1 L. Murray, A. Hipwell. The impact on the child of maternal psychiatric disorders occurring after childbirth. *Current Obstetrics and Gynaecology*, Vol. 5, 75–80, 1995.

2 *ibid*.

3 D. Hay *et al*. Intellectual problems shown by 11–year–old children whose mothers had postnatal depression. *Journal of Child Psychology and Psychiatry*, October 2001.

4 L. Murray. How postnatal depression can affect children and their families. *CPHVA Conference Proceedings*, October 2001.

5 S. Seeley, L. Murray, P. J. Cooper. The outcome for mothers and babies of health visitor intervention. *Health Visitor*, April 1996.

6 A. Sluckin. My baby doesn't need me: understanding bonding failure. *Health Visitor*, November 1993.

7 L. Murray. *op.cit. CPHVA Conference Proceedings*, October 2001.

8 Quoted in C. Tatano Beck. Postpartum depressed mothers experiences interacting with their children. *Nursing Research*, March/April 1996.

9 N. Mohrbacher, J. Stock. *The Breastfeeding Answer Book*. La Leche League International, 1997. P. Stanway, A. Stanway. *Breast is Best*, Pan 1996.

10 A. Dunnewold, J. Crenshaw. Breastfeeding and postpartum depression: is there a connection? *Breastfeeding Abstracts*, May 1996.

11 D. Hay *et al. op.cit.*

7

Puerperal Psychosis – One or Two in Every 1,000

'After just two days, it became clear to everyone that something wasn't right ...'

People around a mother who has puerperal psychosis – a severe and often dramatic mental breakdown after childbirth – may see that something's not right some time sooner than the mother herself.

'Within minutes of leaving the delivery ward, my daughter Sarah was ringing up friends and relations. When I visited later that day she was jumping in and out of bed and undressing the baby so we could examine every inch of him. The second and third day she was exactly the same, and on the fourth she gave me a dozen letters to post. I was waiting for the baby blues to quieten her down, but instead she got more and more excitable and talked an awful lot of nonsense ... a photograph taken on the steps of the hospital revealed a wild look in her eyes ... the first visit to the doctor was after I found 14 nappies in the bucket one morning, having emptied it the night before.'

Sarah was diagnosed as having a manic–depressive type of puerperal psychosis, with highs that sent her behaviour over the top, and lows which left her feeling and acting vacant and unresponsive.

This mother's experience was rather different. She had a second form of psychosis that involved bizarre illusions and obsessions: 'I started to think my brother, who had died five years before, was somehow reborn in the baby.'

And this mother told *Essentials* magazine in February 1997 that she had feared being abducted by aliens: 'Then something told me to bath the baby. First I had to scrub the bath three times. It was like a ritual. I cut a piece of my hair and put it in... I then tossed all his clothes up into the air. When they landed, I looked at the creases and one seemed like a face. I thought that one would be safe to put the baby in … I thought I was evil and had no control over what was happening.'

Kate, a mother writing in the April 2002 edition of the newsletter from Action on Puerperal Psychosis, believed the health professionals who were trying to help her 'were on the side of evil and trying to kill me.' She was desperately frightened... and then after medication and a long sleep, she woke up feeling 'terribly embarrassed for the way I had behaved.' Some women with this form of psychosis see bright lights, images on the ceiling, and hear messages coming at them. They feel their illusions are real, and their dreams may have a powerful significance that everyday life does not.

A third group of women have a psychosis that seems more like very severe postnatal depression of the type described in the rest of this book, but it may have other symptoms like pervasive anxiety.

One mother, for example, told me she became obsessed with routine. She wrote down everything the baby did, every time he fed and how many minutes he spent on each breast. On her mother's advice she switched the baby to the bottle, but then she just became obsessed with keeping everything clean. 'I was terrified I was letting germs into the bottles.'

Not all clinicians would put this last type of experience into a 'psychotic' category, in fact, as someone with these symptoms still has a tenuous grasp of reality, while finding reality impossible to deal with. Some doctors would diagnose her as very severely depressed, and not as having a puerperal psychosis, though it's clear someone so unable to 'cope' with everyday life is undergoing a serious mental disturbance.

Hospital Treatment for Puerperal Psychosis

The first form of treatment is usually drugs, followed by, or combined with, admission into hospital. In addition to drugs, electro-convulsive treatment (ECT) is occasionally used.

We take it for granted that mothers and babies should be together if one of them goes into hospital, but unfortunately, this may not be possible in every case because of a lack of accommodation. A recent survey showed that only about a fifth of health authorities in England and Wales had a special mother-and-baby unit for psychiatric admissions. About half of the authorities said they routinely admitted mother and baby pairs to a general psychiatric ward – an option which has been called 'inferior and unsafe' by the Royal College of Psychiatrists.[1]

Having said that, it's not easy to be certain if every mother should be with her baby at all times; not enough research has been done on the long-term effects (see note in Questions and Answers, page 121).

A very few women may be at real risk of harming themselves or their babies, under illusions that the baby is a threat, evil, or that they themselves are evil or don't deserve to live. In these cases, mothers and babies need very special careful observation, and possible separation.

But too often, the stories of women who have harmed their children are treated sensationally in the media – like the tragedy of Andrea Yates, of Texas, who drowned her five children in June 2001. This was publicised as being puerperal psychosis, yet the doctors at her trial referred to 'schizophrenia and depression with psychotic features.' Andrea Yates may not have had the right sort of care for her long-standing mental illness for many years. Supporters of women with puerperal psychosis have been angered by the way her case has been reported[2] – and the way it has been presented as some sort of typical example of postnatal illness. I know I myself was contacted by several newspapers and radio stations at the time of the tragedy, wanting my views as a commentator, on 'this woman in Texas who killed her children because she had postnatal depression'.

Hospital treatment isn't always needed, and some mothers can be carefully looked after at home, with the support of community health professionals.[3]

Drug Treatment

I have heard a number of accounts of drug treatment that has seemed worse than the original illness. It does appear that it can take a few 'false starts' before women find the medication that does them more good than harm.

'They used a cocktail of medicines which turned me into a zombie.'

'The drugs had powerful side-effects; I started convulsing and screaming.'

Wendy Hawthorne is a health visitor who wrote about her experiences in her professional journal, hoping to give some insights to other professionals: 'My medication was self-cancelling. The side-effects of the antidepressants caused sleeplessness and those of the sleeping tablets caused anxiety. They did no more than keep me spiralling downwards.' (*Health Visitor*, December 1977)

One difficulty is that a mother needs powerful drugs to keep her symptoms under control – and the more powerful the drug, the more powerful the unwanted effects, too. Some strong drugs are unpredictable in their impact.

When the right drugs are used, they may allow a mother to start functioning more normally, and she may be able to come home and share in the care of her baby, perhaps with the support of a community psychiatric nurse or other help.

Effects on the Mother and Her Family

Puerperal psychosis is an especially horrible form of mental illness. While women who have had a history of mental disturbance are more at risk, it can hit anyone, though it's definitely more common in first-time mothers. This difference is partly because of the fact that some women decide to limit their families to one child, as they are too anxious about a repeat episode to risk it – just one indication of the effect on women and their partners, who may have both hoped for more than one child.

Being in the grip of a disturbance like this puts enormous strain on partnerships, especially as the baby's father may be the one trying to arrange for substitute care, or having to take time off work to care for the baby – and support an extremely disturbed partner. In Sarah's case, her husband had to take his baby son to lectures at college, 'hiding' the carry cot at the back and hoping he wouldn't wake up. Another mother told me her puerperal psychosis put 'an enormous strain on my marriage. We have had therapy as a result, and that has helped a lot.'

You Usually Get Better Quickly

The usual time for recovery after an episode of puerperal psychosis is quite short – with the right treatment, it can be as little as two to six weeks according to one recent paper, though many women take longer than this.[4]

According to some authors, periods of relapse – when the mother starts getting worse again – is possible though, and some researchers have found this appears to be more likely when the mother's periods return (which suggests a hormonal link)[5]. Women who have had an episode of psychosis may find their doctor feels they should continue with treatment for a year to try to reduce the possibility of relapsing.

The mother who needs most long-term support is the one whose psychosis has happened after previous episodes of psychosis unrelated to childbirth. She is likely to have continuing difficulties with her mental health, and with her parenting.

Women who've had one episode of puerperal psychosis may have a 20–25 per cent risk of it happening again.[6] The drug Lithium may be successful in preventing this, though this is still being researched.

Signs of Puerperal Psychosis

- ❑ The mother starts behaving in a way that strikes other people as odd very soon after the birth – often in the first days, and certainly within the first four weeks.
- ❑ She may have hallucinations.
- ❑ She may have illusions or strange dreams she feels are real.
- ❑ She may be extremely depressed and unable to relate to her baby.
- ❑ She may be excessively energetic, talking non-stop, writing down her thoughts, rushing around cleaning, or similar.
- ❑ She may develop obsessions about germs or tidiness.
- ❑ She may attribute evil motives to her baby or to herself.
- ❑ She may think her baby has been sent for a religious or spiritual purpose.

Questions and Answers

Q. DOES PUERPERAL PSYCHOSIS HAVE ANY EFFECT ON THE BABY LATER ON?

A. Basically, we don't yet know. Because puerperal psychosis is so rare, it's been difficult to gather together large enough samples to judge what the impact on a baby or child might be. The other problem is that most women spend time in hospital. This means some babies will experience separation from their mothers, or, if they've been admitted together, they will have had care at least some of the time from hospital staff. How do we know we are not measuring the impact of early separation or hospitalization, and not puerperal psychosis?

Some studies show that there's no long-term impact on children as they grow – but it's been suggested that this could be for one or both of two reasons: because (a) in the most severe cases, the babies are often separated from their mothers, and they are protected from the adverse effects of their mothers' illness, notably, the difficulty mothers may have of relating to their babies (see page 105–8) and (b) because mothers who have had 'manic' episodes make a quicker and fuller recovery.[7]

References for Chapter Seven

1 Quoted in G. Alcock, P. Nolan. Maternal mental health 1 – puerperal psychosis. *Modern Midwife*, December 1997.

2 Action on Puerpueral Psychosis Newsletter, April 2002.

3 M. Oates. The development of an integrated community-orientated service for severe postnatal mental illness. In R. Kumar, I.F. Brockington (eds). *Motherhood and Mental Illness: Causes and Consequences*, Wright, 1988.

4 G. Alcock *op.cit*.

5 I.F Brockington. *Motherhood and Mental Health*, Oxford University Press, 1998.

6 S. Oke. Psychiatric disorders after childbirth – prevention and treatment. *Changing Childbirth Update*, September 1995.

7 L. Murray, A. Hipwell. The impact on the child of maternal psychiatric disorders occurring after childbirth. *Current Obstetrics and Gynaecology*, Vol. 5, 75–80, 1995.

8

You Will Recover: Sources of Support

'Listen, accept, reassure ...'

If you think you may have postnatal depression or any form of post-natal distress:

- Find someone you can trust to talk to – this could be a friend, a relative, your partner, your health visitor, midwife, doctor.
- Accept that nothing you are feeling is your fault.
- Think of ways you can start caring more for yourself.
- Socialise with other people if you can, but at places you feel comfortable.
- Accept you will get better – but it may not be overnight, and you may need help from other sources. You may suffer setbacks on your road to recovery.

Don't try to do it alone; if you have any sources of support, use them.

If you are supporting a woman with postnatal depression:

- ❏ Try to let the woman express her feelings of anxiety and fear freely. Try not to dismiss these fears, no matter how irrational – to her they are very real.

- ❏ Women with postnatal depression find it hard to cope. Try to ensure someone is with her as much as possible. If you feel the woman is potentially at risk when left alone, contact her healthcare worker. It may be possible to arrange some short-term group support too.

- ❏ Try to show consideration and sympathy, no matter how tired and fed up you may feel.

- ❏ Encourage and raise her self-esteem whenever she makes an effort or achieves something. Take care not to sound patronizing.

- ❏ A woman suffering from postnatal depression may find it difficult to reason or think logically. Please continue to listen, taking care not to be dismissive of what she says.

- ❏ Encourage her to go out with friends, without the children, but don't force her to do anything she does not feel up to doing. She may find large gatherings too stressful.

- ❏ Appearing too efficient or capable is likely to make her feel a failure.

- ❏ Try to be patient, no matter how hard this may be at times.

- ❏ Don't say things like 'Pull yourself together' and 'You don't know how lucky you are'. She is only too aware of this and already feels guilty about it.

- ❏ Try not to point out shortcomings, unfinished jobs or an unkempt appearance.

- ❏ Try not to show shock or amazement at anything she says or does.

- ❏ Do not be tempted to advise, diagnose, counsel or judge.

- ❏ Remember, it can be tiring and difficult to support someone suffering from postnatal depression. You may also need support!

(Taken from the NCT's Postnatal Depression Support Pack.)

Support Organisations and Sources

of Information

Action on Puerperal Psychosis
The University of Birmingham
Department of Psychiatry
Queen Elizabeth Psychiatric Hospital
Mindelsohn Way, Edgbaston
Birmingham B15 2QZ
0121 678 2354
www.bham.ac.uk/app
Co-ordinates research into puerperal psychosis; has a twice-yearly newsletter.

Association for Infant Mental Health (UK)
120 Belsize Lane
London NW3 5BA
020 7435 7111
www.aimh.org.uk
Predominantly professional organisation that encourages and disseminates research about the psychological health of babies and their parents.

Association for Postnatal Illness
145 Dawes Road
London SW6 7EB
Helpline 020 7368 0868
www.apni.org
Information and telephone support for women with all forms of postnatal depression from women who have recovered.

MAMA (Meet-a-Mum Association)

Waterside Centre
25 Avenue Road
London SE25 4DX
Helpline 020 8768 0123
www.mama.org.uk

Counselling, practical support and friendship to mothers suffering from postnatal depression, plus practical mother-to-mother support. Many groups in all parts of the country.

Marce Society

PO Box 30853
London W12 0XG
www.marcesociety.com

An international society for the understanding, prevention and treatment of mental illness related to childbearing. Mainly professional membership.

MIDIRS

Midwives Information and Resource Service
9 Elmdale Road
Bristol BS8 1SL
0117 925 1791
www.midirs.org

Regular Digest for members. Other members, benefits include a comprehensive database of topics relating to maternity and baby care; literature searches.

Get in touch with your GP's surgery. Health visitors and midwives also keep information about local sources of support.

MIND (National Association for Mental Health)

Granta House
15-19 Broadway
London E15 4BQ
Information Line 08457 660163
www.mind.org.uk
Support and information for people in all forms of mental distress, and their families.

National Childbirth Trust

Alexandra House
Oldham Terrace
London W3 6NH
Enquiry line 0870 444 8707
Breastfeeding Line 0870 444 8708
www.nctpregnancyandbabycare.com
Branches and members almost everywhere. Antenatal classes, breast-feeding counselling, postnatal support. Some specialist groups, including groups for the support of mothers with postnatal depression.

SANE

1st Floor
Cityside House,
40 Adler Street
London E1 1EE
Saneline 0845 767 8000
www.sane.org.uk
Help and information about serious mental illness and support to sufferers and their families.

Useful websites

Apart from the websites listed above with the names of their organizations, it's also worth looking at:

www.pndtraining.co.uk/aboutus.htm
(Training in the detection and treatment of postnatal depression.)

www.babyblues.freeserve.co.uk
('Beyond the Baby Blues')

There are also many e-mail lists and online newsgroups offering support with postnatal depression. You can find some through www.groups.yahoo.com *if you type 'postnatal depression' into the search engine that will appear on the home page.*

Bibliography

The books I have referred to or used as background during the writing of this book include:

Jean A. Ball, *Reactions to Motherhood: The Role of Postnatal Care* (Cambridge University Press, 1987)

I.F. Brockington, *Motherhood and Mental Health* (Oxford University Press, 1998)

Elaine Catterall, *Supporting a Woman with Postnatal Illness* (MIND/NCT, 1997)

John Cobb, *Babyshock: a Mother's First Five Years* (Arrow, 1984)

Maggie Comport, *Towards Happy Motherhood: Understanding Postnatal Depression* (Corgi, 1987)

Katharina Dalton, *Depression After Childbirth* (Oxford University Press, 1996)

Jane Feinmann, *Surviving the Baby Blues* (Ward Lock, 1997)

Sheila Kitzinger, *The Crying Baby* (Viking, 1989)

Sheila Kitzinger, *The Year After Childbirth* (Oxford University Press, 1994)

Jane Littlewood and Nessa McHugh, *Maternal Distress and Postnatal Depression: the Myth of Madonna* (Macmillan, 1997)

Anna McGrail, *You and Your New Baby*, first published as *Becoming a Family* (NCT Publishing, 1996)

Roger Neuberg, *Obstetrics: a Practical Manual* (Oxford Medical Publications, 1995)

Ann Oakley, *Social Support and Motherhood* (Blackwell, 1992)

Rozsika Parker, *Torn in Two: the Experience of Maternal Ambivalence* (Virago, 1995)

Jane Price, *Motherhood: What It Does to Your Mind* (Pandora, 1988)

Joan Raphael-Leff, *Pregnancy – the Inside Story* (Sheldon Press, 1993)

Fiona Shaw, *Out of Me: the Story of a Postnatal Breakdown* (Viking, 1997)

Elaine Showalter, *The Female Malady: Women, Madness and English Culture 1830–1980* (Virago, 1987)

Vivienne Welburn, *Postnatal Depression* (Fontana, 1980)

D.W. Winnicott, *Babies and Their Mothers* (Free Association Books, 1988)

The periodicals and journals I have found especially helpful are *British Journal of Psychiatry*; *British Medical Journal*; *Community Practitioner* (was *Health Visitor*); *Modern Midwife* (now known as *The Practising Midwife*); *New Generation*; *Parents*; *Prima Baby*.

Index